CHINDIT INDISCRETION

To all in whom there yet burns the spirit of Gideon and the Three Hundred.

Judges vii : 7

THE AUTHOR

CHINDIT INDISCRETION

by

J. H. DENNY

CHRISTOPHER JOHNSON

LONDON

The livelong day Lord Marmion rode:
The mountain path the Palmer show'd
By glen and streamlet winded still,
Where stunted birches hid the rill.
They might not choose the lowland road,
For the Merse forayers were abroad,
Who, fired with hate and thirst of prey,
Had scarcely fail'd to bar their way

Canto Third. *Marmion.*
Sir Walter Scott.

First Published 1956
Second Impression 1956

SET IN 12 ON 13 PT. GARAMOND AND PRINTED AND MADE IN GREAT BRITAIN BY PAGE BROS. (NORWICH) LTD. FOR CHRISTOPHER JOHNSON PUBLISHERS LTD., 11/14 STANHOPE MEWS WEST, LONDON, S.W.7

CONTENTS

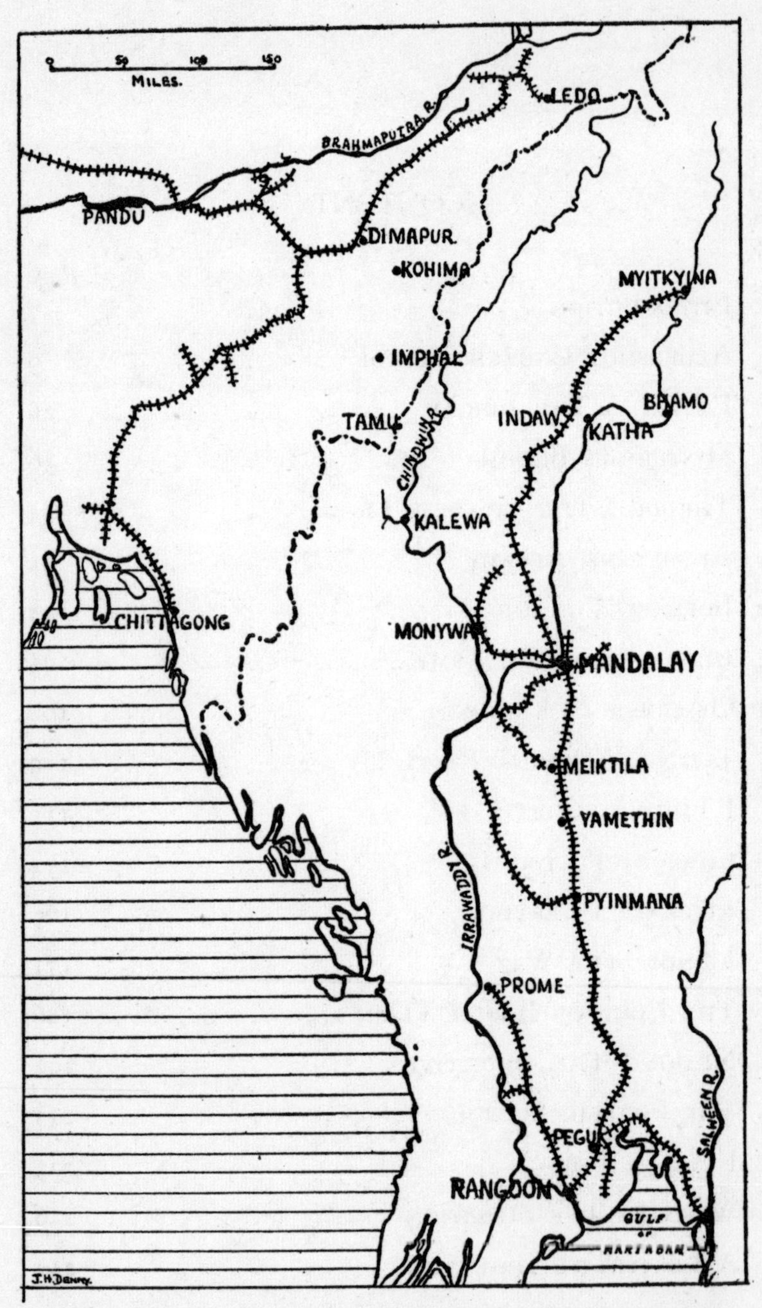

DIAGRAMMATIC MAP SHOWING THE SCENE OF THE AUTHOR'S ADVENTURES.

INTRODUCTION

TWO days after the Japanese launched their treacherous attack upon Pearl Harbour they invaded Burma. Seeping along forest paths, disguising themselves as Burmese, using every trick learned in their years of butchery in China, these uncouth and ruthless men came to rape and plunder.

Within a short time Rangoon, the main port and channel of supply, had fallen, and the Imperial and Chinese forces in the country were forced to withdraw northwards. This withdrawal continued as the Japanese advanced with astonishing speed in a series of outflanking drives, until General Slim's First Burma Corps, and General Stilwell's Chinese troops made their respective ways, together with nearly one hundred thousand refugees, through the dreaded Kabaw and Hukawng Valleys, and over the wild jungle-clad hills to India.

A lull followed, and then General Wavell launched his abortive 1943 offensive in the Arakan. At about the same time Brigadier Wingate led three thousand British troops, his famous Raiders, on a thousand mile trek into enemy occupied Burma, to create such havoc as to frustrate any Japanese attempt at invading India in 1943.

Throughout that year both sides prepared feverishly, the post-monsoon campaign being opened by General Stilwell's forces who commenced to push steadily through the Hukawng Valley. Then the XIVth Army struck in the Arakan, and the Japanese countered with a violent thrust which ended in failure. Meanwhile, the second Wingate expedition was secretly preparing, and at the same time the enemy were putting the finishing touches to their most ambitious—and final offensive plans. In early 1944 these two operations were launched almost simultaneously, Wingate's Chindits occupying the area to the rear of the Japs opposing Stilwell's drive on Myitkina, the terminus of the Burma Railways, and General Mutaguchi, the Jap Commander-in-Chief, invaded India, by way of Imphal.

The outcome is history. After bitter fighting, the Japanese were thrown back and, from that time onwards, were unable to check the advance which began as soon as the Jap offensive was beaten to a standstill, and ended with the fall of Rangoon in May 1945, resulting in the killing of over half of all the Japanese killed in the entire Pacific war.

This is the story of the unusual adventures of one British Officer, one of Wingate's Chindits, during the three critical months at the beginning of 1944, when the fate of India and the whole trend of the War in the East trembled in the balance.

ALDERSHOT CHURCH PARADE

I HAVE an idea that the bottom of Bombay Harbour is carpeted with pith helmets—of that peculiar archaic pattern which I always associate with Gordon of Khartoum. It may even be that lower down is a layer of War Office pattern spine pads, jettisoned by an earlier generation of British soldiers. It was a source of never-ending amazement to me that the authorities in England seemed not to be aware that the Army in the East had virtually abandoned the sun helmet in favour of the salt tablet, and continued to send out convoy after convoy of troops, all equipped in precisely the same manner. It took none of us long to realise that the wearing of the issue-pattern helmet attracted the crowds of shoe-shine boys, fortune tellers, hawkers, touts, beggars, that perpetually hovered within striking distance of all British troops in India like a powerful magnet, marking as it did the uninitiated, the greenhorn; the newly-arrived Sahibs with much money and little sense. So it was that I leaned over the rail of the transport *Glengyle* and added my contribution; wondering as I did so what the future held in store for me.

The War seemed far away from Bombay, the streets were filled with gleaming modern cars and there was plenty of everything in the stores to buy—provided of course one had sufficient money. A row of ancient guns, minus breech blocks, stamped 'Krupps' 1870' lined the jetty where we disembarked and lent a certain emphasis, in their utter uselessness, to the fact that the War was a long way away—on the far side of the vast sub-continent of India in fact. But it was soon to come very much nearer to me.

On the following day we arrived at the British Base Reinforcement Camp at Deolali, and there the atmosphere was just a little different, in many ways vaguely reminiscent of Aldershot, which had been my last station before leaving England, insofar as a dusty sandy plain, surrounded by strange eroded hills, could ever resemble any part of England. It was a khaki shirted and shorted sort of Aldershot, it is true, but the same strange devotion was still paid to caking equipment with the evil compound called Blanco, ample space for which had apparently been found in the heavily-laden supply ships which had run the gauntlet of the U-boat packs on the long journey from England. I even received a visit from the local representative of—of all things—the Prudential Assurance Company who vainly attempted to insure my life, not, of course, to include war risks.

Soon after arrival I was informed that I was posted to 2nd Field Coy., R.E., then near Saugor in Central India; and a further interesting fact was also revealed to me: namely that I was a volunteer for a secret and dangerous operation.

* * *

To say that I was surprised is to put it mildly; my feelings went much deeper than that.

I had been a newly-commissioned subaltern at Aldershot, when it fell to my lot to participate for the first time in the weekly Church Parade to St. George's Church. This took place with due ceremonial as befitted a town like Aldershot. My batman had performed right nobly upon my Service Dress, raising it to a high standard of carefully creased elegance, which was matched only by the glossy sheen of my boots and Sam Browne, so that I felt a certain pleasurable anticipation at the opportunity of occupying so prominent a position.

When the great day arrived I arrayed myself in all my finery and made my way to the Parade Ground. For the benefit of those not familiar with Aldershot, it must be explained that this particular Parade Ground lay almost opposite St. George's Church, and that the Parade fell in on the far corner of the Square, so that the longest possible journey could be made. I was in command of the first of the three companies on Parade. On arrival, I found the men already fallen in, in line, by companies, one company behind the other. I took my place in the front of my company, and the Parade Commander, with his escort of two N.C.O.'s, took up position in front of me. It was only then that I realised that I was not as familiar as I should have been with the procedure; somehow or other certain important details had quite escaped me.

I knew that I had to turn about to face my company, turn them to the right, and then take up my position at the head of the column thus formed. This I performed without difficulty, but the Parade Commander and his escort were thus invisible to me. For a brief moment a feeling of panic swept over me, as I stood rooted to the ground gazing at the thin line of interested spectators at the edge of the Square: for the life of me, I didn't know what to do next. There flashed into my mind an absurd cartoon I had seen in a magazine: a body of Guardsmen, with the superb discipline of their kind, marching over the edge of a high cliff because their tongue-tied subaltern had forgotten the word of command, whilst the irate Sergeant Major at his side barked: "Say something, Sir, even if it's only Goodbye!" There came to me a vague recollection that I had to march forward on to the road, wheel to the left, and lead the Parade along that road to the crossroads, and there again wheel left and thus come to the Church. My confidence returned, and in clear ringing tones I gave the order to quick march. Reaching the road, I led the column round in a superb left-wheel; and then realised that the Parade Commander, who should have been in front of me, was simply not there.

Once more panic swept over me and my confident military bearing dropped from me like a cloak. Turning my head rapidly, I saw, half-way across the Square heading directly towards the Church and away from the rest of the Parade, the figures of the Parade Commander and his escort. They were marching with great precision under the obvious impression that I was immediately behind them, leading the rest of the Parade. I realised that I should have wheeled left before reaching the road, wheeled left again, and thus have come up behind the Parade Commander. I had undoubtedly committed the *faux pas* of the year, what many of my comrades would have described as an M.F.U., and I was already dimly conscious that I should go down in local history as the man who led the Church Parade the wrong way round.

It says so much for my powers of self-control that I did not turn tail and run; my sole thoughts were of hiding my much diminished head. Somehow or other, I kept on marching, and behind me I could hear the steady tramp of feet—and nothing more; not a whisper, not a snigger came from the men; but I knew what they were thinking and my hair fairly curled at the knowledge.

On I went until I came to the crossroads; there I left-wheeled and arrived at the Church door. Major Stokes, the Parade Commander, was waiting for me: one look at his face was sufficient. "Are you mad?" he hissed. "Wait till the C.O. hears about this little business!"

On the following morning I was called for by the Adjutant, and received a dressing down that left me slightly dazed but otherwise unharmed. I was surprised that the C.O. had delegated this duty to the Adjutant, and even felt somewhat hurt by the obvious implication that I was of so little importance that even reprimands could be administered at second hand. One rather ominous phrase however, stuck in my mind: "—disgracing the unit; making the Battalion a laughing stock. Let me tell you that the Colonel has his eye on you, and will certainly endeavour to find the proper reward for such insolence."

In vain, I attempted to say that it was all a mistake; the Adjutant, and indeed everyone else, seemed convinced that the whole incident had been deliberate, the outworkings of a perverted sense of humour.

There are of necessity some parts of this story that I cannot relate from first-hand knowledge, but one or two hints came my way, and I became aware that, from time to time, in the Mess the C.O.'s eye would rest upon me in a contemplative manner; and I would squirm and wonder. I should imagine that it went somewhat as follows:

(Scene) the C.O.'s office.

"Much in the mail this morning, De Creasy?" (the Adjutant).

"Not much, Sir. There's a signal here from War House asking for the names of suitable subaltern volunteers for special work: no details given."

"What the devil do they mean? Anyway can't be of much importance—some fool to act as bear leader to a crowd of third-rate E.N.S.A. troupers—or maybe somebody for R.T.O. in Wagga-Wagga, or some such place. Anyway who don't we want?"

"Well, Sir there's——"

"I know, that fool—what's his name? That fool who messed the Church Parade up."

"Shall I suggest it to him, Sir?"

"No, send his name in; he'll find out what he's volunteering for when he gets there. Serve the little tick right. The Brig. gave me quite a ribbing about that business."

So it came about that about a fortnight later I was suddenly ordered, after embarkation leave, to report to the R.E. Depot at Halifax, on an oversea posting, *en route*, so it transpired, to India.

* * *

In the few days that elapsed, before my posting to Saugor took effect, I began to learn a little about the strange land of India.

I managed to get about a fair bit, although to my sorrow I was unable to visit Ghandi's birthplace Nasik City which was only a few miles away; the whole city being out of bounds to British troops. Much of the detail of that impression has now vanished but, in the strange manner in which distance lends enchantment, there remains to me an image, vaguely attractive, my personal discomfort being forgotten. I can remember driving down a long, long Indian road, a narrow strip of tarmac with, on either hand, a broad ankle-deep band of white dust and a row of dust-covered waxy-leafed trees. I can almost feel again the pitiless glare of the sun, the inescapable dust clogging my throat, torturing the eyes, and billowing behind in a great white cloud as though the friction of the wheels had struck the heated earth into smoky combustion. There comes upon me the queer sensation of knowing that the self-same road wound on and on forever across the vast peninsular, never stopping, never reaching some real, some logical terminus, passing again and again the huddle of huts which seem more like a collection of beehives, yet hold the population of a sizeable European town. I see the caravans of creaking bullock carts, the lonely Sadhu, the bent pedestrians, trudging ankle deep in the soft clinging dust, the little knots of pilgrims, the frequent family groups halted beneath the trees to eat their meagre allowance of *chapatis,* hearing the sad high pitched greetings between friends and the occasional snatch of mournful song from the fields, as the primitive ploughs, pulled by the sluggish oxen, scratch the pitilessly hard earth in the little plots from which the sadly apathetic villagers coax a pitiful harvest, every stalk bought with the sweat of their brow in grilling labour. I realise again that it was a hard country, a merciless country, a country of untold millions to whom it could give no more than a few handfuls of grain to eat and a few decades of bitter indebted toil for a life; and, for the hope of the future, an awful hob-goblin ridden religion of many-armed gods and goddesses and hideous demons. I remember the wayside shrines, the naked children, the bald and mangy pi-dogs, the earthy smell of the villages, the stench of hot *ghi*, the cow-dung cakes on the mud walls, the screeching monkeys in the mango groves, the glimpse of a minor potentate's Palace, a bizarre monster of towers and turrets encased in peeling pink plaster, surrounded by a broken wall with a pair of massive wrought iron gates at the entrance, one of which had long since fallen away at the top hinge, somehow symbolising more effectively than anything the whole spirit of India. I remember that touch of decay, that detail left unfinished or unrepaired, that spirit of 'failed B.A'ness' which labels the way-side tea stall: 'The Universal Refreshing House', and tells you: "I will happily show you the way soon, isn't it. I was at Calcutta University and I failed to take my Bachelor of Arts degree, so that my English is utterly fluent."

One evening I caught the night train from Deolali Station, and the following day I arrived at the concentration area of the 16th Infantry Brigade. I had a companion for the first part of the journey, a subaltern destined for one of the other Companies, who was as bewildered as I was; he also had made the discovery that he was a volunteer. He was at the time in a slight difficulty, after finding that the bottom of the large tin trunk which contained most of his worldly goods was covered with several inches of melted candle wax in which a miscellany of socks, shirts and other garments was embedded. It appeared that he had been advised—needless to say by an old soldier—to lay in a large stock of candles, since he would find that, in India, they were worth their weight in gold, and in such short supply that he would be able to dispose of them and show a handsome profit. Acting upon this remarkable piece of advice, and in the true spirit of the Merchant Venturers of old, he had packed the lower part of his trunk with candles—and the tropical sun had done the rest.

I arrived to find the whole Brigade ready to move, trained and equipped, tough, burned by exposure, and of a very formidable appearance. I was completely untrained, unacclimatized, and soft from several weeks of idleness on board a troopship—and of course a volunteer!

I was just in time to be issued with the necessary clothing and equipment, and, after one night on a concrete floor without a mattress, I was thrust on board a train *en route* for the Burma Border.

By the time the 16th January, 1944 arrived, we had been travelling four whole days, a dreary business, even for us junior officers in the comparative luxury of a dirty and neglected second-class compartment. At first the train had crawled through the sun-baked countryside of Central India, stopping and starting at all sorts and sizes of railway stations. The pattern of them had by this time become familiar. I no longer wondered at the dust, the filth, the betel-juice stained platforms, the whining beggars, the persistent hawkers of an astonishing variety of goods, and the ubiquitous vendors of tea the Tcha-Wallahs, as I had already come to know them, carrying their tin urns with the charcoal fire beneath and a tray of little unglazed earthenware pots, which would be used but once and then destroyed, to avoid offending the religious susceptibilities of the customers. The sari-clad women with ringed ears and noses, nearly always carrying a naked babe astride their hips, and followed by a small crowd of other children, offered tangible proof of the enormous Indian birth-rate. At every station, scantily-clad coolies swarmed aboard the train before it stopped, in anticipation of engagement for the purpose of carrying our baggage. The sight of the sacred Brahmini cattle, the goats and mangy dogs wandering amongst the milling crowds on the platform no longer surprised me; the cries of the vendors, the shouts and queer high-pitched babbling, rising from the sweating, earthy-smelling mob, no longer sounded strange in my ears: I had lost the power to wonder at the kaleidoscope of colour and drabness, the discordant shouts and cries, the heat of it all, and the clouds of gritty dust swirling up from it: I was tired and jaded from the long journey.

The long steel bridge over the sacred Ganges across which we crawled into Allahabad stirred me a little, and I roused some interest as the dry barrenness gradually gave way to the lush greenness of the Bengal countryside.

We had changed trains soon after that, and continued our journey in a narrow gauge train, the first sight of which surprised me. I marvelled how so large and broad an engine could balance safely on so narrow a track.

We had arrived at Amingaon on the previous night. After a meal, the all too familiar one of hard biscuits, corned-beef, tinned fish and jam, washed down with strong tea made with boiling water from the engine, we composed ourselves for the night, enervated by the sight of the civilian Assam Mail on the opposite platform, through the dining car windows of which we could see chicken being served, and cheered by the prospect of soya links for breakfast in the morning before we crossed the mighty Brahmaputra to Pandu on the Assam side.

Morning came, and I had crawled from beneath the stifling mosquito net, wiped some of the filth from my face in the stinking lavatory with the cistern and the fan that did not work and the cracked mirror, bearing the stencilled legend: 'If you have any complaints, the Guard has a complaint book'—swallowed my portion of the revolting soya links, hard biscuits and strong tea, and dragged together my belongings, preparatory to crossing the ferry.

Many men of the XIVth Army are familiar with that crossing. The station of Amingaon, with its corrugated iron-roofed platforms is set in the flat Bengal countryside and surrounded by wooded hills, precursors of the higher, steeper, more thickly-blanketed hills on the Assam border, some of which can be seen across the broad and sluggish Brahmaputra. Pandu on the opposite side was a mere collection of squalid *bashas* nestling at the foot of one steep, temple-crowned hill, and was surrounded by sprawling railway sidings, from the midst of which snaked the one single riband of steel, the single track metre-gauge railway, along which vital artery poured the very life blood of the armies holding at bay the Japanese invader.

After the usual confusion, the men were sorted out. We all filed down to the crazy bamboo footbridge which wriggled out across the mud and through the shallow water to the hulk alongside which the ferry boat was moored. So, with much hissing and clanking from the archaic engines of the tall-funnelled, flat-bottomed, paddle-wheel ferry boat, we began the crossing.

On the opposite bank, even before the gangways were in position, a yelling horde of grimy coolies and porters swarmed aboard the ferry boat like a cloud of vultures, and retired disappointed when they discovered that we had no bed rolls or vast tin trunks to be carried: our possessions were upon our backs, carried in the large pack worn by every officer and man.

All this takes but a few lines of my paper, but, in actual fact, the whole morning was occupied in this manner. Immediately we were on shore we were marched away to the rest camp, there to be provided with a relatively respectable meal. One little incident stands out in my memory. A large body of Chinese roops was passing through the rest camp on the way to India for training and equipping, having been flown over the Hump from China. They had no arms whatever, and were dressed in faded and tattered padded blue uniforms. Only about one man in six wore boots; most wore straw sandals which contrasted oddly with their blue, knee-length puttees. The Chinese officers were at lunch when we entered the Mess, and they were very nearly as shabby as their men, despite the Sam Browne belts which they wore. It might have been their first meal under Western conditions; nearly all of them looked as if they would have preferred squatting on the floor to sitting at a table; whilst the knives and forks on the tables puzzled them considerably. However, they would not admit defeat, and several of them did really notable execution with the unaccustomed implements, even to the extent of picking up a whole slice of bread on a fork and nibbling away at the edges!

Refreshed we marched back to the station, and were soon on board another train for the final stage of our journey. All afternoon we rattled on at a brisk pace through the Assamese countryside, its many tidy villages and neat bamboo houses compared favourably with any I had seen elsewhere in India. The people also seemed to be much more advanced than the puny apathetic Bengalis; small but well-developed, and of a distinctly Mongoloid appearance. For long periods we passed through jungle which loomed like a green wall on either side of the track. From one side of the train, we could see the beginning of the hills parallel to which the railway runs, and, on the other side, the country stretching away to the river, and the Himalayas beyond, of whose mighty snow-capped peaks we caught an occasional glimpse. Towards the latter part of the afternoon, we began to pass through the well-ordered tea gardens from which comes a large part of the tea we drink.

Now it was evening, and would soon be dark and I sat thinking and wondering, and wondering and thinking over and over again.

I was aroused from my reverie by the bouncing of the train as it rolled across points, which indicated the nearness of a station, perhaps the one where we should detrain, for none of us knew the nature of our destination, apart from the C.O. and possibly the Company Commanders. This did not prove to be so, but something did happen there which was to have a profound influence upon the events of the coming months. This station marked the beginning of my fantastic adventure.

The train shuddered to a standstill alongside a platform of a fair-sized station, and I discovered from the name board that we were at Manipur Road, or Dimapur as it is sometimes called. It was soon apparent that we were not to detrain, and so our meal was prepared. The proceedings were enlivened by the spectacle of the irate C.O. chasing a number of officers out of the Refreshment Room. They apparently having been labouring under the delusion that they were exempt from the ban, imposed upon us all at the beginning of the journey, from going into any such public place, or talking to strangers. This journey was shrouded in secrecy; none of us knew our destination, beyond the bare fact that we were bound for some part of Burma, behind the Japanese lines.

Perhaps it would be advisable if I added a few more words about the composition of this force of which I was a member. We were part of the 16th Infantry Brigade, one of the several Brigades forming the 'Special Force'—'Chindits'—Major-General Wingate's Long Range Penetration troops. Most of the other Brigades were to achieve fame by entering Burma by air in one of the largest and most audacious of all the air-borne operations of the whole War. Each Brigade was sub-divided into eight columns, each of which was a completely self-contained striking force, composed of about half a battalion of Infantry, with attached Engineers—of which I was one—and R.A.F. Signal personnel. Every column was designed to operate behind the enemy lines for a period of several months. Sufficient rations were carried to enable the column to live for seven days; at the end of which period it would be supplied by means of parachute-dropped supplies. As much ammunition and explosives as possible were to be carried, and more supplied by air as necessary. Sick and wounded were to be evacuated by light plane, which would land at suitable points for that purpose. Such supplies as were not carried on the backs of every officer and man would be transported by mules, which also carried the heavy weapons, mortars, medium machine guns, P.I.A.T.'s and medical supplies, wireless sets, charging plants, and the Sappers' tools and explosives.

Every officer and man carried a considerable, and exactly similar, load, consisting of a rubber ground sheet, used for a variety of purposes, even including the construction of small boats, a blanket, two pairs of socks, a pair of canvas rubber-soled shoes, a spare shirt and spare pair of trousers, a *chagul* (canvas water container) and a Mae West (life jacket) for crossing rivers, as well as the seven days' rations, which were usually American K rations, pack rations, the sight of which we came to detest. On top of this load was the usual equipment: mess tin, water bottle, two grenades, a rifle and bayonet and fifty rounds of ammunition, or, in certain cases, a Sten gun instead of a rifle. This made a load calculated to try the strongest, when it is considered that it was to be carried through dense jungles, in a climate which is notoriously trying for white men. Yet it was done; and still another page was added to the tale of Britain's glory by a handful of cursing, grumbling men, largely forgotten by their own fellow-countrymen.

With each column was a detachment of Burma Rifles; a small platoon of Burmese who acted as guides and interpreters; gallant men for the most part, for they were venturing into their own country, often to their own villages, as hunted men, and nothing would have been easier for them than to desert, go back to their own people and obtain great profit by betraying their column to the Japanese. Yet very few did; and it is to their everlasting credit that they suffered the same hardships as their comrades from the far-off British Isles.

I have digressed sufficiently, and now I go back to my story.

Within a very short time, the meal was prepared; the tea being made as usual with boiling water from the engine. We officers congregated round the door of the coach from which our appetising meal was dished out. I can well remember that meal, as well as I can remember the scene on the platform that evening. We had hot soya links, heated by the simple expedient of dropping the tins into boiling water before they were opened, biscuits, jam for dessert, and of course, tea, hot and strong, in enormous green enamel mugs.

For some reason or other, my appetite had failed me that evening, and so I soon broke away from the knot of chatting officers and wandered along the platform to stretch my legs. The platform was crowded with troops in various stages of undress, eating and drinking, laughing and talking, grumbling and swearing, as British troops always do. I walked to the end of the platform, withdrawing from the noisy mob in search of a few minutes peace and quietness. By this time it was nearly dark, and in a few more minutes would be completely so, so, after a few minutes of quiet enjoyment, I decided that I would wander back.

I had just detached myself from the tree against which I had been leaning, when I saw an Indian civilian walk up the inclined end of the platform and come towards me. For some reason or other, I moved no further but stood with my back to the trunk of the tree idly watching him as he approached and then passed me. As I have said, the light was fading rapidly so that I could not see him distinctly, but although I could not describe him accurately I should say that he looked like any one of the multitudinous minor officials, ticket collectors, clerks, and the like, employed by the Railway Company. I vaguely remember that he wore the usual white *dhoti* with a blue shirt flapping outside; a commonplace enough figure. I am persuaded that he did not see me; I was wearing the dark green jungle uniform, and standing beneath a low spreading tree, and it was nearly dark.

After a few more seconds I decided that the train would very soon be starting, and it was high time that I got back to my compartment. Even as I started back I was confirmed in this view by a loud double blast on the engine's whistle. I was now only too anxious to regain the compartment, and so I sprinted along the platform. Before I realised what was happening I had blundered into two figures standing at a little distance from the troops clambering into the train. I was sure that they must have been talking together, so close were they to each other. I at once perceived that one of them was the civilian I had seen a few minutes before, and the other was one of the Burmese soldiers. Immediately it flashed into my mind to ask the soldier why he was talking to the civilian. We had been repeatedly warned not to enter into conversation with any outsider. As quickly as the thought flashed into my brain I realised that it would do no good; none of the Burmese understood English, and I knew no Burmese, and the train was about to pull out. However, I did stop and look at them; when, to my utter astonishment, the Indian turned tail and bolted along the platform the way he had come and the Burmese, dropping something which hit the platform with a metallic clang, dived into the crowd milling round the train and disappeared.

I was certainly astonished; but scarcely suspicious. The conduct of the Indian was rather strange; but there was nothing strange about the haste with which the Burmese private had made for the train. In any case I realised that it was high time that I followed his example. This I did, but not before I picked up the object which had been dropped, by the Burmese I fancied, with the intention of returning it to him at the next stop on the following morning.

So I also dived for the train and regained my compartment. I know now of course that it was my sudden appearance from the dusk, and the realisation that I was an officer (we did not remove our badges of rank until the following day) which had startled them into sudden flight. But of such things, I had at that time no inkling.

After I had recovered my breath, I examined the object which I had picked up, and saw that it was a small statuette of Buddha, made of brass, and about four inches in height, thus confirming my belief that it had belonged to the private who was fairly certain to be a Buddhist. I showed it to my companions, but they evinced little interest, so I dropped it into my pack and forgot the whole incident.

The train rattled on and, after some desultory conversation and discussion of the chances of getting off the train on the morrow, we spread out our blankets and retired for what was to be our last night under a roof for a considerable period.

ENTERING THE JUNGLE

I SEEMED to have been asleep only a few minutes when I was suddenly awakened by a violent banging on the door of the carriage, and by a loud voice, which I recognised as belonging to the Adjutant, exhorting us 'to get out of it'. It took me some minutes to collect my scattered wits and realise that this was the end of the journey, and that the sooner I did collect my few belongings and 'get out of it' the better. I imagine that nowhere in the world was there a more disgruntled body of men than that particular train load at four o'clock in the morning. We had imagined that we should detrain in the usual fashion some time during the day; a glance at any map of Assam shows that Manipur Road is not very far from the terminus of the Bengal and Assam Railway. To make matters worse a glance from the window showed that we were not even at any sort of station; or for that matter showed no sign of anything beyond the dimly seen inexpressibly gloomy jungle: and it was raining!

The compartment was a scene of complete confusion, or would have been if it had been possible to see anything at all. It is scarcely necessary to add that the lights, like the fans and the previously mentioned cistern, did not work. We poked and pushed one another, scrambling and scuffling in a wild attempt at finding our scattered belongings: trousers, boots, socks, and all the other odds and ends.

I do not have to try very hard to imagine myself back to that morning, and I smile now when I think of the spectacle we must have presented. We were still heavy with sleep and our equipment was scattered in the wildest confusion around the compartment. I know that I had the greatest difficulty in finding my bush hat, and I was almost in despair until I realised that it was suspended by the strap from one of the ceiling fan guards. The matches we had, being of Indian manufacture, put on their usual three act performance: they either did not light, or the heads broke off the sticks, or occasionally they behaved with tolerable docility and obliged with a miniature explosion and flash of flame. One of my companions sallied forth from the coach in a brisk manner, only to discover that there was no platform; but not until it was too late. There was a loud yell as he disappeared from sight, and a still louder yell as he hit the wet ground and rolled into the ditch, accompanied by a metallic clatter as the various bits and pieces of his equipment fell from his person. I fear that he received little sympathy; in fact we derived a morbid satisfaction from his misadventure.

At length we managed to get ourselves on to the narrow strip of muddy ground separating the train from the dripping jungle. It was almost completely dark and raining hard. I found myself one of a mob of bewildered soldiery. No officer near me had the slightest idea of what was happening, and it was quite impossible to sort any order out of the rabble around us. For some minutes I stood in a state of indecision, wondering if I could possibly find the C.O., when suddenly the whole crowd began to surge in one direction and I ceased to bother and surged with them.

I learned afterwards that the C.O., having satisfied himself that everyone was awake, had gone to one end of the train and as soon as every man appeared to be out called to the men nearest to him to follow him; and the rest followed suit: an interesting example of the herd instinct put to good use. In any case it would have been impossible to have done the thing in an organised manner. It was dark, the space was so restricted, and only a few of the senior officers knew anything about the whole business.

The cursing and grumbling mob shambled blindly along the edge of the track for some little distance and then turned at right angles to the railway into a narrow jungle path. We moved along in this manner for perhaps a mile, or a little more, and then came out on to a broad paved road, which I discovered afterwards was the Ledo Road.

To my surpise no attempt was made to halt there, the mob turned right along the road, and I, perforce, went with them, feeling I remember, that this was all wrong and I ought to do something about it. Luckily I did nothing and trailed along with the rest. Very soon vehicles, which I perceived to be U.S. Army vehicles, began to pass at regular intervals, and I thought that a very widely dispersed convoy was passing. After proceeding in this manner for perhaps half an hour, by which time I was beginning to feel the weight of my pack, I could see in the growing light that the vehicles were stopping for a short time ahead of me, and moving off again as soon as the next vehicle came up with the one preceding it. After a while I realised that the vehicles were picking up the men at the head of the straggling column and moving off with them. I was very nearly at the end, although I had not realised it, and by the time I was picked up almost everyone else had been taken off.

The truck I boarded moved away at considerable speed for about three miles, and then turned off the road into a track running through the jungle. After getting well out of sight and sound of the road the truck stopped in a clearing and we 'debussed'. I discovered that the apparent confusion was at an end, and, at a little distance away, breakfast was being served to some of the earlier arrivals.

Then it dawned upon me that, far from being what we usually called a 'shambles', our arrival had been very neatly organised and executed. None of us had known our destination, therefore we could not have told anyone, and no one would be waiting to see who we were when we did arrive. We arrived in the dark, and we had not detrained at any station where interested eyes might notice our arrival. The trucks were not parked along the road waiting for us, but must have been assembled elsewhere as if forming up for a ordinary convoy run, and the way we were picked up was so contrived that no civilian, and very few troops, would know anything about the whole business.

Another point sprang to my notice: I heard one of a number of apparently American troops who were hanging about the place speaking in a very English accent, plentifully interspersed with that Anglo-Saxon epithet dearly beloved by many British soldiers. So, to avoid attracting attention, the advance party had been dressed in American uniforms, we being in an American area; furthermore we had been transported in U.S. Army vehicles.

I must say that all this inspired quite a lot of confidence in the Staff preparation that had gone into the beginning of this operation, and I, for one, felt that it augured well for the success of the whole business.

By this time the rain had ceased. I had been scarcely conscious that it was raining all the time that I had been walking along the road, my mind being too full of the novel manner of our detrainment, but I realised that I was soaked to the skin and extremely uncomfortable. There was nothing that I could do, so I attempted to forget it by busying myself with the several little jobs that needed to be done.

I must explain that I was the third officer of the 'Commando' Platoon; a rather misleading name, for we were simply the Sappers combined with the Infantry Pioneers, and our role was to carry out such minor Engineer work as was necessary, and be responsible for any demolitions that were undertaken; not forgetting that we were expected to act as Infantry as well. I was an afterthought, the reinforcement officer, and as such I was actually surplus. It had been decided to take the reinforcements along with the column in view of the obvious difficulties of communication. The Platoon Commander was one Captain Mitchell, a regular ex-ranker, and a typical one at that. I think that he had been a C.S.M. before he was commissioned. He was something of a rough diamond, not very well educated; but for all that an efficient officer and popular with the men.

Breakfast over, the officers were taken to view the site of bivouac. We set off along a narrow path leading from the clearing straight into the jungle. Perhaps it would be better if I described it as a tunnel rather than a path, for the jungle was thick on either side and overhead as a wall of green. It was not what I had expected from the accounts of tropical jungle which I had read. Here were no gaudy flowers, no myriad birds and insects, no monkeys swinging in the branches overhead, no little animals slinking through the undergrowth. The place was as silent as the grave, and more indescribably gloomy than any vault or dungeon. I saw no sign of life whatever, and no sound broke the heavy stillness of the oppressive atmosphere beyond the dripping of water through the vegetation. It was only half light; yet overhead the sun must be shining with tropical brilliance. Above, the unbroken green roof shut out even an occasional glimpse of the deep blue sky, the heavy blanket of green seeming to press down, inducing an unpleasant sensation of claustrophobia. Yet there was life here and death beneath our feet, the vegetation seeming almost to pulsate with the feverish struggle for existence. Here the competition was fierce and the stakes high. Above was an abundance of sunshine and air; below, the soggy carpet of dead and decaying vegetation told its own tale. Trunks of giant trees grew close together, their crowns out of sight somewhere above the growth of lesser vegetation. There was bamboo in massive clumps; hundreds of stems as much as twelve inches in diameter to a clump; and, growing alongside, the broad long leaves of the plantain struggling for existence in so dismal a place. Creepers festooned every tree and bush; some like fine wire in size and strength, and others resembling massive ships' cables. Here and there lay the rotting trunk of some giant which had been overcome in the struggle for existence. Occasionally, the long dead hulk of a tree still stood vertically, or leaned over at a crazy angle, held in the twining mass of creepers which had in all probability killed it. Aerophytes nestled in the crook of the branches of every tree, trailing their long aerial roots into such space as there was.

It did not take me very long to decide that it was the most unpleasant place that I had ever seen, and without doubt the most unhealthy. The idea of living in it for even a short period was far from attractive.

The bivouac areas were allotted by the simple expedient of pacing a given distance along the tortuous path and informing a particular Platoon Commander, with an airy wave of the hand at the jungle, that this constituted the platoon area. The site for the Commando Platoon was soon allotted, and we retraced our footsteps to bring up the men. Then we fell to hacking some sort of a living space from the jungle.

It was hard work as we, officers and men alike, chopped away at the tough, clinging vines and bushes. Although the temperature was not particularly high, it was oppressively humid and, within a very short time, we were soaked with the perspiration which streamed from every pore. By mid-day we had made considerable progress and it was possible to move about fairly easily between the bigger trees and the clumps of bamboo. Then it was time to think of constructing some sort of a bed with a shelter for the night. Some men worked in pairs, making a double bed, using their two ground sheets to form a kind of tent overhead. I regarded my own particular effort as being something of a masterpiece, and it may be of interest if I describe it.

I selected a spot between two fairly small trees about seven feet apart and eighteen inches in diameter. I then obtained two pieces of bamboo about nine feet in length and lashed them to opposite sides of the trees with strong creepers, so that they were parallel and about three feet from the ground. Across these two pieces of bamboo I laid, and lashed, short pieces of split bamboo—and there was my bed. Two similar pieces of bamboo were then lashed in position, one piece about four feet above the others, and the other on the opposite side of the trees about three feet up. Short pieces of bamboo, placed across the latter two pieces, formed a sloping surface over which I laid my ground sheet; thus forming a roof. As my ground sheet was only about six feet long, and the trees a little more than seven feet apart, I thatched the remaining part with leaves of the wild plantain. More plantain leaves, some of which must have been fully six feet in length and eighteen inches in width, hung down the side as curtains to keep the rain from splashing in sideways. I spread my blanket on my 'bed' with the remainder of my worldly goods at the foot under the thatched roof, and there I was, relatively comfortably housed. As I surveyed my handiwork, I reflected that, only a few short months previously, I should have recoiled in horror at the thought of sleeping under such conditions. Aldershot and its environs seems to be part of another world. Certainly no homeless vagrant in England slept in such a manner as we ex-civilians, once used to all the comforts of modern civilisation. Yet, such is the adaptability of human nature, I felt quite satisfied with my lodging for the night, suspecting that I would soon be spending nights under much less comfortable conditions.

Whilst some of the men produced really sound structures, others were not so successful, and many improvised beds collapsed during the night. In other cases, the fact that a flat ground sheet would fill with rain water was overlooked; only to be forcibly impressed upon the unfortunate individual beneath by a flood of water at some unearthly hour. It sounds amusing now, but it was no joke at the time.

The Burmans, who were mostly Chins—hillmen from the North of Burma—excelled at this improvised construction with bamboo, and even built themselves huts fitted with benches and tables. They also furnished the Officers' Mess, if a small clearing in the jungle can be so grandiosely termed, with more benches and tables.

By dinner time, about five o'clock, a camp had sprung into existence in the heart of the jungle. In the short space of a few hours one patch of ground had become the Cookhouse, another the Guard Room, and yet another the Quartermaster's Stores. The very jungle path had a name, and was duly sign posted: 'Leech Alley'—with good reason as I was to discover when I removed my boots.

Darkness descended rapidly at about six o'clock, and, as we had no other means of illumination, numerous fires of dry bamboo, taken from the heart of a clump, sprang up all over the place. There was no danger that they would reveal our presence, since the jungle which dimmed the light of the tropical sun would effectively hide the glow of a smoky fire of bamboo.

I was very tired and I sought my luxurious couch early. Almost everyone else was of a like mind, and within a short time the fires began to die out one by one, and darkness descended upon the little community of Englishmen, Scots, Welsh, Irish and Burmese.

I have mentioned leeches. The place abounded with them. It was only necessary to move a few yards from the path and glance at the ground to see at least a dozen of the horrible creatures, arching themselves towards one's feet in a very determined manner. We wore the usual stout ammunition boots, with short puttees bound tightly round the ankles, and they were as effective as could be expected in the circumstances. Even so, I usually found, when I removed my boots for the night, that at least one had managed to insinuate itself between the layers of puttee, during the course of the day, only to be squashed into a bloody mess, after it had sucked some of my blood and swelled as a result. After a little while, I could feel the slight nip as they dug their teeth into my flesh, and a vigorous jab with my other boot had the effect of squashing them before they had drawn any blood. I have on occasions actually seen one effecting an entrance through one of the eyelet holes in my boots, in spite of the fact that it was almost completely filled by the leather lace. They were horribly persistent creatures, dropping from the foliage overhead, or waiting at the side of the path on the leaves and branches to be brushed off by an unsuspecting passer-by. It was quite useless to attempt to pull them off, once they had taken a grip; the only result was that the head was torn from the body leaving the head still firmly adhering where it would continue to suck blood. Furthermore, the mouth parts, embedded in the skin, caused an infection resulting in a jungle sore. However, there was a very simple remedy; it was only necessary to apply the lighted end of a cigarette to the leech to cause it to relax its grip and drop off—a match would do also. The puncture bled profusely for some minutes, after the creature had fallen off; the explanation being that they inject some substance which prevents the blood from clotting.

Yet even these loathsome creatures were surpassed in horror by the ticks; although they were fortunately not so numerous. They had the delightful habit of burrowing beneath the surface of the skin and then performing a sort of tunnelling operation. This was extremely painful, even though they are only tiny creatures. They also caused a septic sore, unless dug out with a sterilised needle.

It was particularly disconcerting to discover that a tick was inside one's blanket; that really did cause some fun.

I slept the sleep of the just that night, whatever that is, undisturbed by such horrors, and as soundly as ever I slept between the clean sheets of my own bed in distant England.

MYSTERIOUS BUDDHA

MORNING came and the day's work began. There was much to be done to make the muddy hole in which we found ourselves more or less habitable. We Sappers were busily employed in a variety of jobs; cutting down the steep bank of a near-by *chaung* to form steps to enable the men to go down to the water to wash, improving the tortuous path forming the axis of our camp to make it less worthy of the title of 'Leech Alley'; whilst I, personally, was engaged with a small party in constructing a bridge over a muddy *chaung,* so that the mules might be brought into the camp easily. Our bridge consisted of nothing more elaborate than four suitable tree trunks with branches laid across them, and a surfacing of wet earth reinforced with twigs and leaves. I was proud of my bridge, for the trees, which were quite large, were cut down with nothing more formidable than a folding saw.

The day passed quickly enough; being notable only for the fact that it commenced to rain again in the evening, consequently there was nothing to do after the evening meal except to retire to our hovels. It was a miserable meal. In the outside world it was raining hard, judging from the amount of water which dripped from the foliage overhead into the 'Mess' where we stood in a disconsolate group. Our shirts were soaking wet, and our sodden mud-caked boots squelched mournfully in the inches-thick layer of decayed vegetation and slime beneath our feet. It was almost dark; the green of the jungle all round had faded into a dirty grey murk beyond the smoky glow of the crackling bamboo fire around which we huddled. The bamboo benches were streaming with water, and, as a wet seat was an added discomfort, not to mention the voracious leeches with which the wet surface literally teemed, it was not even possible to sit down to rest our aching legs. Our attempts at keeping the sticky mess of our hot meal dry were ludicrous in the extreme. I more or less succeeded by almost burying my nose in the mess tin, bending my head forward so that the broad rim of my bush hat acted as a roof over my food.

A few words about that most sensible form of headgear will not be out of place. They were light and the broad brim provided protection against both sun and rain, and, when new, were very smart in appearance. Our own hats served a variety of useful purposes besides the one of a head covering, being frequently used as buckets for carrying water and as feed bags for the mules. This treatment, as may be imagined, did not improve their appearance and, within quite a short time, they lost their original smart outline and reverted to a conical shape. Most of the men carried their spare bootlaces round the crowns of their hats plaited into fantastic patterns, and as the brim usually waved up and down, like Atlantic rollers, the general effect was quite charming. The only headgear that I have ever seen which even remotely resembled our bush hats was in England—adorning the head of a ragged scarecrow in a ploughed field.

By this time almost everyone had assumed a distinctly cut-throat appearance; although the real pitch of perfection in this respect was not reached until another week or so had elapsed, and before privation turned these swashbucklers into sick, haggard wrecks of humanity. Shaving was optional, and, because of the difficulties in obtaining razor blades, it was not long before a clean-shaven face was the exception rather than the rule. Some men produced surprising efforts; several men with dark hair sprouted distinctly ginger beards, and, as a hair cut was an even more difficult matter than a shave, they presented a curiously piebald appearance. Very ordinary-looking individuals sometimes sprouted the most magnificent-looking beards. One muleteer in particular grew a wonderful pair of moustaches and a pointed beard which made him resemble Sir Francis Drake. The general result was villainous, and I hate to think of the effect our appearance must have made upon our wives and lady friends, could they have seen us. Our hats and our beards, our stained and torn clothes, and the variety of instruments of destruction, adorning our persons, combined to make us a desperate-looking crowd indeed. Every officer and man had his rifle and bayonet or Sten gun, and most people carried some sort of a knife as well, not to mention the two '36' grenades bulging from the pockets, or wherever the individual chose to carry them. The equipment was slung about our persons in the manner best suited to the owner thereof, and would surely have been the despair of any Regimental Sergeant Major of the old school. Many men had turned their large packs into a variety of rucksack, so that the load hung low on their backs, with pads of sorbo-rubber under the shoulder straps to ease the load.

I must mention that we were issued with apparatus for assisting us to escape, should we be taken prisoner, or if we were ever lost. We each had a map of yellow silk about the size of a pocket handkerchief, with the map of Upper Burma printed on one side, and the map of Lower Burma on the other side. Being made of silk, it could be folded into a very small compass, and could then be hidden in the lining of the trousers or concealed under the hat band—the *pugri*—and none but a careful search would reveal its presence. Then we had a tiny magnetic compass about half an inch in diameter, and we were also issued with two special trouser buttons. To all intents and purposes the buttons were the usual type of brass thread-cutting trouser buttons provided on Army trousers, but one had a little pimple on the bottom and the other a small depression in the same place. To use them as a compass, for that is what the buttons really were, it was only necessary to cut them from the trousers and balance one on top of the other, the pimple fitting into the depression and acting as a bearing, allowing the upper button to revolve upon the lower one, until it came to rest with a tiny punch mark pointing North.

On the following morning I realised that our numbers had increased, and I discovered that two more columns had arrived during the night. In another day or so, the whole Brigade had arrived, and the mules also appeared. I never discovered what stratagem was used to cover the arrival of the mules, but I have no doubt that some ingenious arrangement was devised for the purpose.

For some time I completely forgot the incident which occurred at Manipur Road, until I chanced to find the little statuette at the bottom of my pack. I took it along to Captain Chit Kin, M.C., commonly known as 'Chicken', the commander of the Chin Recce Platoon, and asked him if it belonged to any of his men. I handed it to him and he examined it curiously and immediately said:

"But this is not right."

"What isn't right?" I asked.

"This thing, this Buddha," he replied. "The attitude is not right for a Buddha, in fact I have never seen one like it before."

Then he went on to explain to me that a statue of Buddha always has the hands in a certain position, whereas this particular specimen had the hands down by the sides. Of course, it was so, and I then realised myself that there was something wrong with it. We examined it very closely and discovered that there were some marks on the base which looked rather like Chinese or Japanese script. We could make nothing at all of them, and, although I later showed them to several of the officers, none could tell me what they were. Captain Chit Kin took the little image away with him and made enquiries amongst his men. In a little while he came back with a puzzled expression upon his face.

"It does not belong to any of my men," he said in his precise English. "What is more, they say that they have never seen it before, and in any case they would not own such an incorrectly made Buddha."

"But I saw one of them drop it," I insisted. "At least he must have dropped it."

"No Buddhist would own such a thing," he replied.

"It's all very queer. Let me see if I can pick out the man."

To this he readily acquiesced and obligingly paraded his whole platoon. I carefully inspected the face of every man, but in the end I had to admit failure. To me they all looked alike. My eyes, unused to the sight of bland Oriental features, told me nothing. After all, I had only had a fleeting glimpse of the man in the dusk. I wandered up and down in front of the men for some little time trying to pick the man out, but again failed. Finally I gave it up as a bad job, although I was far from satisfied. I vaguely knew that there was something wrong, but, for the life of me, I could not see what it was. I tried to persuade myself that the man had merely been indulging in a little forbidden conversation with the civilian and was afraid to admit it now; but this did not explain how the soldier had been in possession of a Buddha which

Chit Kin solemnly assured me no self-respecting Burmese Buddhist would even dream of owning. I was so concerned that I thought about it for some time, until the pressure of events drove it from my mind, and I completely forgot that it was reposing at the bottom of my pack.

During the whole of our stay at Lakapani it rained at intervals and we were as often wet as dry; the inclement weather being a constant topic of conversation, for it was not the monsoon season and the unseasonal rain had not been expected. It made things very unpleasant, and we all began to be heartily sick of the inaction, and even more so of the dank hole in which we were living. It is almost unnecessary to say that we were not allowed to leave the bivouac area; the only men allowed on the road were the ones in American uniform.

* * *

It was about the sixth day after our arrival when I was informed just after the mid-day meal that the Adjutant wanted to see me. I went along wondering what he wanted, and hoping that it meant something was going to happen at last. It did, but scarcely what I had expected.

"The C.O. wants you to go off with the mules tonight," he said when I presented myself. "The A.T.O. has gone sick, and you are the only spare man we have."

"But I don't know anything about mules," I objected horrified at the very idea. "I didn't do any training with you at Jhansi, and besides I'm a Sapper."

"You don't need to know anything," he snapped, nettled at the invidious comparison. "Sergeant Ross knows all that is necessary, and you need not think that this is beneath you, just because you happen to be a

Sapper. Anyway it's been decided that you are going, and you will go."

"Well what have I to do then?" I asked.

"The Intelligence Officer will supply you with the necessary maps; he knows all about it. Your rations have been laid on and will be ready. The C.O. will give you your instructions at three o'clock, and you will be starting as soon as it is dark; so get your stuff packed."

I was extremely dissatisfied, but there was nothing that I could do. I had been continually told that it was not necessary for me to know anything ever since I had joined the column. No training whatever had been given to me, whereas the other officers and men had been training hard for months. I was completely ignorant of the elaborate Battle Procedure which they had been practising; but what was far worse I was not as fit as I should have been, having spent five lazy weeks on board ship, and only having been in India for a very short time.

I packed my scanty belongings and went along to the mule lines. I found the whole place in a turmoil, as the muleteers strove to harness the unwilling mules. Threading my way gingerly between the prancing mules, and, sniffing distastefully the unaccustomed 'horsey' atmosphere, I searched for Sergeant Ross. Eventually I found him and started to discuss the journey, confessing that I knew nothing about mules and their peculiarities. Fortunately he appeared to be quite capable, and after a while I left him to complete the arrangements.

At three o'clock I presented myself before the C.O. and received my instructions. I found that I was not to travel alone, but that a Lieut. Smithson, the A.T.O. of the other column, our companions on the journey from Jhansi, would be bringing his mules along as well. We were to travel as one party, a total of about one hundred and sixty men and mules, as far as a place called Nam

Yung Bridge; taking seven days over the journey, moving only by night, and resting during the hours of daylight. Each night's journey would be fourteen or fifteen miles, with halts at certain definite milestones where suitable camp sites were reputed to be found. Two trucks, one for the rations and the cooks, and the other to carry the food for the mules, were to accompany us on the journey, travelling independently of the slow-moving mules. That was all, and it sounded simple and fool-proof, but alas—'the best laid schemes of mice and men. . . .'

It was about half-past five when we started, slipping and sliding along the greasy path in the direction of the road, and only half light as we passed through the clearing and along the uneven track. Smithson and I walked at the front, and behind us came the long line of laden mules, one after the other, and bringing up the rear was Sergeant Ross leading a pony, with other sergeants leading ponies at regular intervals along the line of the column. It was hoped by this means to control the long, unwieldy file, adjusting our pace to prevent the tail from straggling on the information given from time to time by the sergeants who would act as D.R.'s.

Finally after a journey of seven days, in which I learnt that there was a great deal more to mules than I had ever suspected, we reached Nam Yung and there we found the rest of the two columns waiting for us. They had come from Lakapani, our first camp site, by truck the previous night. The new camp was again well off the road, and could only be reached by fording a stream three times in the course of a half-mile journey along the bottom of a narrow valley. In this place we spent several days making the final arrangments for the real start of the expedition. Every day supplies and rations had to be carried to the camp from trucks on the road, and it was a strange sight to see the long line of officers and men, for everyone, including the C.O., worked, wending their way up the valley and fording the stream, carrying boxes and cases. A great part of the time was spent resting and amusing ourselves as we pleased. A good deal of fishing was done; much of it by the reprehensible method of dropping a hand grenade into the water and waiting for the stunned fish to float to the surface after the explosion. A good deal of ammunition was also used in shooting. In a very short time we of the mule party had recovered and we were ready for the next part of our journey.

THROUGH THE JAPANESE LINES

WE started off again on or about the 5th February. This time we travelled in the correct order of march, by platoons within the column, and for the first part of the journey we were to travel with our companions of the other column. The rest of the Brigade was to follow by pairs of columns at intervals of one day. Some of the secrecy was removed, and we knew that we were making for a certain spot on the banks of the Chindwin River where we were to make a crossing. Each day the proposed route for the next twenty-four hours was explained to the men, so that they might have a chance of rejoining the column should they become separated and lost. Three men did become 'lost' on the first day. It transpired afterwards that they had deliberately detached themselves from the column, and hidden until everyone had passed, and then they made their way back to the road. I did not see them again until several months had passed when I gave evidence against them at their court martial; by that time many of their comrades who had not shirked their duty were a heap of mouldering bones in the jungle.

I must mention in passing that Major-General Wingate himself paid us a visit on the day before we moved off. He spoke to us all for a few minutes; a singularly uninspiring address for so forceful a character. It was principally about the care of our weapons during the coming months, and, as most of us were greatly concerned at what appeared the slim chance of caring for ourselves during that period, it left us completely cold.

Yet his personality made an impression upon me. He seemed to radiate an air of ruthlessness, and there appeared very little of the milk of human kindness in his face as he stood before us. The zealot was slightly below medium height, thick-necked and sturdily-built, and his eyes were deep-set and his mouth hard. There was nothing of the patriarch in his appearance as is suggested by the photographs of him wearing a beard. Many stories were circulated concerning his ruthless methods, and generally speaking he was feared. Despite all this, he was respected in rather a grudging manner, as was shown by the luridity of the curses and imprecations that his name evoked daily. Within a short time the great man, for such he was, was dead, killed in a plane crash.

It was early in the morning when we started; the long line of men and mules slowly wending its way along the narrow valley to the road. It was a sight that I shall never forget. It was the real beginning, and every man and beast carried a full load. At the head walked the C.O., looking exactly like any of the other men, without badges of rank, unshaven, and carrying the same bulging pack, his Sten gun hanging from one shoulder, and the 'Walkie Talkie' (small wireless set), with which he maintained contact with his platoon commanders and controlled the column, hanging from the other shoulder. Behind him, in single file, heavily bearded, grim and silent came the perspiring men, and the mules with their boxes all in order ready to swing into action at a moment's notice. Near the head of the column, acting as pace setters, two draught bullocks, laden like the mules, plodded along at a steady two and a half miles an hour, a speed which could not be increased under any circumstances, as anyone will realise who knows bullocks.

We followed the road for a short distance and crossed the Nam Yung Bridge which was still a-building. Chinese engineers were hewing huge trees into square baulks by hand, whilst others drove piles into the bed of the stream. Then we turned from the road and began to climb the precipitous hillside. Some of the Commando platoon had been out several days previously cutting the dense undergrowth and vines, and making steps in the steeper places. Even so, the going was desperately hard, the slope averaging forty-five degrees, and the mules had even greater difficulty than the cursing, perspiring men, loaded as they were, in climbing up. Hour after hour went by, and still we climbed and scrambled and dragged up the mules, half a dozen men being sometimes necessary to haul and push one mule; scratched and torn, caked with filth, tormented by insects, and half blinded by the sweat trickling down into our eyes, gasping, panting and cursing with the exquisite torment of prickly heat, breaking out around the tight waist bands and beneath the dragging packs of most of us. The last part of the climb was the worst of all, and we actually had to unload the mules and manhandle them and their loads up, since they could not climb as they were. The undergrowth was little obstacle to us who followed, having been flattened and cut by the leaders, but it was thick all around us and must have impeded those ahead very considerably.

It was past mid-day when we reached the top, and there we were forced to rest for some time to recover. Afterwards the going was a little easier, the hill top being like a blunt knife edge and the vegetation quite thin, as is often the case with those otherwise completely jungle-clad hills. Along this knife edge we moved at a steady pace until it was time to halt for the night.

We prepared and consumed our meal and, after carefully burying and hiding all litter, moved about a mile away, as was our invariable custom for we never bivouacked where we lighted the fires—fires are liable to attract attention. We looked for trouble only when we wanted it. There we spread out into the usual position of all-round defence, and built our improvised beds for another night in the jungle which mysteriously came to life with the fall of darkness. I never ceased to marvel at the way in which the day-long dead stillness and seeming emptiness changed into a weird jumble of sound, as soon as the sun went down, so that the air was filled with the hum and chatter of insects, the croak of frogs and the rasp of cicadas; barking, howling, braying, and the rustle of foliage as some creature of the night crept past. It was all so different, and at first rather frightening, but we became as used to it, as to all the other peculiarities of our jungle life, with the passage of time.

For six days we travelled, living on the rations we carried, making painfully slow progress and averaging somewhere round about ten miles per day. Everything remotely resembling a man-made track was carefully avoided, thus exploiting the Japs' known preference for the jungle tracks and trails. It was the most critical part of our journey. Everything depended upon our ability to slip undetected past the Japanese. Our route lay across a stretch of the wildest and least-known country in the world, which at once assisted and impeded us in our task. The jungle, clothing almost every inch of the hills, was so dense that our whole column could easily have passed within a hundred yards of the Japanese, with little danger of detection; yet that same density which served as a cloak for our movements, often made it necessary to hack a path through the clinging undergrowth. What exhausting labour it was! We had to work with our packs upon our backs, and struggle up the side of a hill, or descend a steep declivity at the same time. It was almost as tiring for the men behind as for the men actually hacking at the undergrowth. They could only make progress in fits and starts as those ahead repeatedly came upon clumps of undergrowth too thick to struggle through.

I could feel that it was telling upon me, and see the same effect in the faces around me. Despite the heavy beards, it was possible to see a definite tightening in the lines of the features, as cheek bones became more prominent and eyes sank deeper into their sockets until some of the men began to look really haggard. We lived in an atmosphere of constant tension, knowing that the enemy was never very far away, fancying always that every bush concealed a lurking Jap and wondering, wondering what lay ahead. Even our sleep at night was not so restful as it should have been to enable us to cope with the exacting demands made upon body and mind alike.

On the fifth day it was noticeable that we were going downhill more often than we were climbing; a sign that we were getting through the hills. Another sign was the increasing depth and width of the *chaungs* we had to ford. At first they were seldom more than knee deep, but by that time they were waist deep, and deeper, and we had constant difficulty in keeping our weapons dry and serviceable. Our clothes were as often wet as they were dry, little hardship in itself, but the wet foliage near the *chaung* banks teemed with voracious leeches and we suffered considerably.

Finally, on the sixth day, we reached the Chindwin, having successfully slipped through the Japanese 'lines'. In the six days of our journey we had described the arc of a circle, having struck off at right angles from the Ledo Road, later to veer round so that we travelled parallel with the axis of the road. In other words, we journeyed round the rim of the bowl of the Hukawng Valley, through which the Chinese forces were then pushing slowly forward.

Before us lay the formidable barrier of the Chindwin, gleaming in the hot sunshine, wide and deep, with a very fast current making it impracticable to cross by swimming, even assisted by our Mae Wests. This contingency had been foreseen and preparations made accordingly. A small party was waiting for us with collapsible boats powered by air-cooled motors, which had been dropped by parachute at some other spot to avoid revealing the crossing to the enemy, and then floated down the river. The link-up was made with suprisingly little difficulty, considering the density of the jungle, but we were greatly assisted by being in wireless communication with each other.

For one day we rested, in the wild, lonely spot with the great river before us and all round the gloomy jungle and the sinister hills, making preparations for the crossing. A supply drop had been arranged to take place on the day before we did the night crossing of the river. By this means, it was hoped that, even though the Dakotas might be observed dropping their loads, we would be across the river and away before the enemy could investigate. A patch of relatively open ground on the top of a low hill at a little distance from the river was chosen, and marked ready for the drop to take place. I was one of the party detailed to receive the supplies which were to drop, like manna, from the skies. Punctually we heard the drone of aero engines and soon the Dakotas, those maids of all work, were circling overhead, and the billowing white parachutes were bearing the precious supplies down to us. At first all went well, and it appeared that the parachutes would land on the desired spot, but when they were about fifty feet from the ground a current of air caught them, and carried them away from us down the slope of the hill. We had miscalculated badly. The possibility of the existence of such a current of air should have been foreseen. As a result, our precious supplies were scattered far and wide, and, despite a lengthy and exhausting search, not more than half of them were recovered. This was serious, for we dare not linger for another drop to be made; that would be asking for trouble, and, as supply drops could not usually be made more frequently than once in seven days, it looked as though we should be on short rations during the coming week; and that proved to be the case.

That night the crossing was made. The men were taken across in the boats which ran a ferry service, towing the swimming mules behind. It was no easy matter to coach the nervous animals into the dark water and hitch them to the special rails strung between two of the boats, but it was done successfully, and every man and mule landed safely of the far bank. The final act was to stave in the bottoms of the boats, so that they sank out of sight beneath the fast-flowing waters of the great river, thus obliterating the traces of our crossing. In that manner we crossed our Rubicon—yet not as Caesar did—one day we hoped to return. Then we moved at a little distance from the river and, on the following day, recommenced our journey.

Soon we were amongst hills as steep, and jungle as dense as any on the far bank of the river, and it was a constant struggle to make progress. The routine of column life began to be familiar to me, and it became natural to sleep on a rough bed of bamboo, to do guard duties at all too frequent intervals, to live a life of self-effacement, both individually and collectively, striving always to conceal the presence and passing of a large body of men and animals. Fires had to be lighted in places where the smoke would be invisibly dispersed; tins, cigarette packets, and all other litter had to be buried, and great care taken even when washing in a *chaung* to avoid exposing the white nakedness of our bodies to some chance aerial, or terrestrial, observer. All this, and more, became my life, and it was difficult to realise that there was anything in the world besides jungle, hills and leeches. We lived a life as hard and as dangerous as any soldiers of the British Crown have ever lived. We were hunted men.

Our only safety lay in our elusiveness; quite incapable as we were of fighting a pitched battle with our limited supplies of ammunition. Our aim was to out-do the enemy at his own game; exploiting, as I have said, his preference for the tracks and trails of the jungle, going where civilised man had never gone before, carving our own way through the wild country, to strike hard and suddenly and then disappear as quickly as we had come taking no prisoners, and scarcely expecting to be taken alive; knowing well that our chances, if sick or wounded, were slight indeed. Yet there was scarcely a man amongst us who did not feel that he would survive, come what may.

The first losses occurred soon after we crossed the river. when one of the muleteers was injured so badly that he died shortly afterwards, and his mule had to be shot. It happened whilst the man was leading his mule along the edge of a deep, steep-sided *chaung*, apparently in perfect safety. Without any warning, the animal lost its footing and slipped over the edge, knocking the man down with it to the rocky bed of the *chaung* twenty feet below, falling on top of him, crushing him badly, and breaking its own leg. The unfortunate man was dead within an hour. This first death depressed us considerably, bringing us face to face with the reality of our position. We scraped a shallow hole for him, and then moved on again.

We were heading for the Myitkyina-Mandalay Railway, a distance of something like eighty miles, as the crow flies, although we were not crows, and would cover a far greater distance before we actually arrived there. Very soon afterwards other forces of Chindits did actually proceed to the same area in a truly crow-like fashion, to make landings on the now famous airfields of 'Broadway, Chowringhee, and Aberdeen', but it is not my purpose to record those exploits. The Brigade of which I was a member, Ferguson's 16th Brigade, later joined up with those air-borne forces which played such havoc with the Jap lines of communication in the rear of the troops opposing the Chinese-American advance on Myitkyina—but I was not fated to be numbered amongst them at that time, and I digress.

The first actual contact with the enemy was made somewhere round about the 17th February, and, although it was not to be the last brush the column had, it was to be my last, and the beginning of a strange chain of events which finally culminated little more than a month later. We had been successful in avoiding native villages, and had not seen a single living soul since we left the Ledo Road, so we had good cause to believe that the enemy knew nothing of us. It was now decided to make our presence felt.

* * *

The Japanese had a ferry somewhere above the point where we had crossed the river, with a motorable track leading up to it from a small station on the railway. At one point this track crossed an unusually large *chaung,* by means of a bridge, which, we had been informed, was of timber construction. That bridge was our objective. Its destruction would disrupt the flow of supplies to some of the Jap forward troops. We intended to see what damage our 112 lbs of guncotton would cause. Apparently, there were difficulties in the way of destroying the bridge by aerial bombardment, besides which our sudden appearance so far in the Japanese rear would be inclined to upset them!

It was more than probable that the bridge would be guarded, it being of some importance, and, before any plan of attack could be made, it was necessary to discover exactly what opposition would have to be faced. A *recce* party was accordingly despatched when we were within half a day's journey of the bridge; the remainder of the column resting and making the necessary preparations.

The main part of the task would, of course, fall upon the Sappers, consequently we were very busy sorting over the explosives, fuses and booby traps. Everyone was full of suppressed excitement at the prospect of a real clash with the enemy, and, as this was the first action in which the great majority of the men had taken part, an undercurrent of nervous tension ran through the whole column.

The *recce* party returned late in the evening, and reported to the C.O., who immediately called a conference of his platoon commanders to thrash out the details of the method of attack. Very soon after the conference came to an end, every man was familiar with these details, as was our usual custom whenever possible. The scheme seemed to be good and relatively foolproof.

The *recce* party had been able to penetrate to a position from which they could overlook the bridge and approach roads, and study the construction of the bridge through field glasses at their leisure. The bridge was somewhere about a quarter of a mile in length, spanning a stream which was about two hundred yards in width, and had mud flats on either side. It was of mixed timber and steel construction; piled timber trestles, supporting inverted steel Warren trusses over which was laid timber decking. As we had only one hundredweight of gun-cotton, it was resolved to attack the timber trestles, demolishing four of them, thus dropping five of the spans into the stream and creating a gap of about one hundred feet. Grenade mines were to be buried in the earth-road, on the approaches to the bridge, to blow up a few vehicles, and the area sowed with a large number of a particularly fiendish brand of booby trap. The latter were in the form of a small pointed metal tube about six inches in length, open at one end, and pointed at the other. This tube was pushed into the ground, open end upwards, and a spring loaded firing device dropped in, and on top of this a special bullet rested, with the top of the bullet just protruding from the tube. The device was then lightly covered with earth ready for an unsuspecting soldier to step upon. The effect of this was to cause the firing device to strike the base of the bullet, thus detonating it and shooting it in a vertical direction. If the man was lucky, the bullet merely passed through his foot, but, if he was unlucky, it went up his leg, causing a nasty wound. It was altogether a diabolical piece of work. The advantage of this particular variety of booby trap was the speed with which it could be planted in position; not more than fifteen seconds being necessary to plant each one.

The bridge appeared to be guarded by a detachment of about twenty soldiers, and at least one officer, identified by means of his sword, showing that a good deal of importance was attached to it. Two sentries were posted at each end and were changed at intervals of four hours. The guard lived in a number of small bamboo *bashas*, which were fortunately situated on our side of the bridge.

The problem was to silence the sentries on the far bank, before they had an opportunity of getting away and giving the alarm, no easy matter in view of the length of the bridge. The men on the near side and the men off duty in the huts could be dealt with, if they were taken by surprise, almost everything being in our favour so far behind the Japanese forward troops.

It was resolved to make the attack very early in the morning, by the light of the moon which was then a little past full, at a time when the sentries would not be particularly alert, and when little or no traffic should be using the road. The first thing to be done was to cut the telephone wires. That accomplished, the sentries must be silenced, the detachment dealt with, and then we could set about preparing the demolition charges without hindrance. It was hoped to have the whole job finished by full daylight to enable us to make our getaway in the light of day. That may sound rather strange, but it must be remembered that it is next to impossible to make any progress in jungle country in the dark, and we could easily deter possible pursuers by scattering a few booby traps in our trail.

The river was too deep to ford, and the current strong, so it was decided to deal with the sentries on the near bank first—silently—meanwhile another party would surround the huts ready to dispose of the occupants. Then two men dressed in the tunics and helmets of the near-bank sentries would cross the bridge, their disguise enabling them to get within Sten gun range of the far bank sentries. The burst of Sten gun fire would be the signal for grenades to be tossed through the windows of the huts, thus disposing of the Japanese off duty. Immediately afterwards a party was to double across the bridge to establish a road block on the far bank approach road; whilst another road block was set up on the near side. We Sappers could then get to work, fixing the charges on the bridge, and laying the mines and booby traps.

We moved into position on the top of a hill overlooking the road and bridge as darkness was falling, following the route taken by the *recce* party on the previous day, and then waited.

The time passed very slowly as we waited, tense, expectant, and more than a little fearful, for the moon to rise. At long last, it lifted itself above the surrounding hills like a huge yellow lantern, bathing the whole scene with soft light. I have never been privileged to see a more beautiful and peaceful scene than that spread out at our feet. There was sufficient light to reveal the wild grandeur of the hills rolling in broken masses around us, the jungle-clad slopes dark and mysterious; and the tree tops below us, the roof of the jungle, appeared to be solid in the moonlight, so that it seemed possible to walk across them to our destination which was plainly visible. The broad band of the stream gleamed like silver, with the long black bulk of the bridge silhouetted sharply against it, every trestle pier clearly defined. Around us, the multitudinous insects filled the air with a constant buzz and chatter and an occasional bark or howl, weird and unearthly like the cry of some earthbound spirit, floated to our ears. Occasionally a murmur of soft rustling sound like the gentle lap of little waves upon the sea shore rose from the tree tops below, swaying in the gentle breeze. Once I heard the faint sound of men's voices, and a little peal of laughter, so soon to be hushed in violent death, floating up from the valley. I fingered the cold barrel of my Sten gun and tried to shut the horror of it from my mind. A peaceful scene indeed, as under the trees on that hill top we huddled, intent upon death and destruction, our eyes gleaming wildly in the dim light as the gentle breeze sighed and the yellow moon looked down and God in His Heaven. . . .

Eventually, it was time to move, and the various parties began to slip off down the hill into the jungle. The mules were left with the muleteers, who also guarded the packs left behind by the Infantry to enable them to move and fight unhindered. The Sappers left last of all, carrying our packs upon our backs filled with tools, explosives, rope ladders, pieces of wood, string, wire and all the other accessories needed to prepare a demolition. I had not completely emptied my pack, having left my Mae West and one or two other small objects in the bottom—fateful action—with the vague idea that I might need them, before packing nine grenade mines on top. I was in charge of the far bank mine-laying booby trap party.

After about half an hour of blundering and scrambling, we reached a point just clear of the approach road, and there we waited whilst the Infantry moved on.

I cannot describe what happened as the guard was overpowered, for I did not see it, but I can imagine how the two sentries were decoyed by some ruse into the hands of the waiting stranglers, or on to the point of a bayonet. I can also imagine how the huts were silently surrounded, the men waiting with the 36's in their hands, pins removed, whilst the telephone line was cut and the dead sentries stripped of tunics and helmets. I can see in my mind's eye the two men, picked for their small stature, wearing those tunics and helmets, with their trousers bound tightly to their legs to simulate the Japanese knee length puttees, a long Japanese rifle slung across their shoulders, and a Sten gun concealed in the crook of their right arms, padding boldly across the bridge in their canvas shoes and approaching the unsuspecting Japs on the far bank. But I did hear the sudden sharp rattle of the Stens, followed, almost immediately, by the dull explosions of the grenades, and then I ceased to wonder as we sprang to life, and doubled along the road towards the bridge.

The need for concealment had gone, the entire Jap detachment was dead, and we shouted directions, and flashed torches as we doubled across the bridge. I ran behind three men carrying a medium machine gun, with two others carrying a PIAT alongside, and others with boxes and belts of ammunition hurrying forward to set up the road block on the far side of the bridge. My own party consisted of six men, and we followed the Infantry across the bridge, whilst the largest party of Sappers stopped in the middle to fix the charges.

The bridge seemed to us a terrific length, burdened as we were, and our pace slowed down as we approached the far bank. At last we arrived panting for breath, and straightway commenced to lay our mines and traps across the whole width of the road and the verges at the side, with as much speed as was consistent with a reasonable amount of safety; which is not very fast, as anyone familiar with such devices will appreciate. It is only too easy for the layer to be caught by one of his own traps, particularly when the laying is being done at night.

We finished our task after about half an hour's work, during which time there had been no sign at all that the alarm had been raised. It was doubtful if there was an enemy camp within several miles, and the noise of the firing had apparently gone unheard. I was just about to order my men to return to the bridge when I heard a sharp exclamation from one of them. I turned quickly and saw a light somewhere ahead dipping and jerking in an erratic manner. For a moment I wondered what it could be, and then I realised that it was the light from the masked headlamps of an approaching vehicle.

Within a few seconds, we had picked up our tools and retreated behind the road block, there to wait for whatever was coming. The light grew steadily stronger, and then disappeared as the truck passed behind some obstacle, to reappear about half a minute afterwards. I gripped the steel barrel of the Sten gun I was holding convulsively, in an agony of fearful anticipation, as the light grew steadily stronger and the muffled beat of an engine became audible. Then I relaxed, as I realised that it was nothing more than an ordinary military lorry, driven by a blissfully unsuspecting driver, who was probably half asleep. I heard a quick whisper from the far side of the narrow road where one of the M.M.G.'s had been set up, followed by a staccato roar as it opened up in a long burst of fire. The lights were abruptly extinguished, and the black bulk of the vehicle, now plainly visible, turned sharply from the road and crashed into the ditch.

The chattering machine gun stopped as abruptly as it had started, and then there was silence as we waited. Nothing happened. There was no sign of life in the wrecked vehicle, so we simply assumed that the driver was dead and carried on as if nothing had happened. My party withdrew to the bridge to assist the men working there, and we threw ourselves into the task of completing the job, as soon as we could, before the approaching daylight brought more traffic on to the road.

Finally the guncotton slabs were all tied to the piles, two slabs to each, the primers and detonators inserted, and the electric leads paid out to the exploder on the bank. Mitchell had detailed me actually to fire the charges, and I set up my firing position on the side of the sloping embankment, at a little distance from the end of the bridge, but too near the demolition for my liking. However, there was no alternative, since the leads would reach no further, but I thought that I would be reasonably safe since we were only blowing timber, the blown fragments of which seldom carry very far. I carried out the routine tests for continuity, despite the fact that there were men still on the bridge, a practice that was frowned upon in the days of my training. I got a kick on the Test Set galvanometer straightaway, and connected the leads to the exploder—again ignoring the safety precautions—and waited.

The dawn was just breaking, and I was beginning to feel very tired and hungry, when a regular fusillade of shots—on our side of the river—made me start violently. Then I knew we were being attacked. Somehow the alarm had been raised after all. For what seemed an age I waited with growing anxiety whilst the firing went on, then, in the intervals of firing, I heard the heavy beat of an engine and what sounded unpleasantly like the rattle of tracks—tank tracks. I was soon confirmed in this view by a sudden bang, followed by another bang, obviously the firing and burst of a small shell.

The Infantry were running along the road above me, and my fingers were simply itching to push down the exploder handle, as I wondered if I would never get the word to fire. Then I heard the voice of Mitchell above me:

"O.K. let her have it. Then get away quick."

It was enough for me. I raised myself to my knees to get the maximum output from the exploder, and putting all my weight behind it, I forced down the handle. Immediately there was an ear-splitting roar, and the ground shook beneath my feet as I crouched down as low as I could. A blast of air swept past, and then a rain of debris crashed into the undergrowth around me, making me flatten myself even lower, vaguely wishing that I was wearing a steel helmet. Two or three seconds elapsed, and then, just as I was about to pick myself up and run for it, I was struck a violent blow on the back of the head; I saw a blinding flash, and knew no more.

ALONE AND AFRAID

MY next sensation was that of crawling very slowly and very painfully from out of a deep black pit, with the noise of the explosion still ringing in my ears—or so it seemed to my fuddled wits. I was quite sure that my head was in two parts, hinged together at the front, and opening and shutting at the back like a book, with a dull pain shooting through it from back to front every time it closed. I had no idea where I was, or what had happened, and I felt so ghastly that I cared little.

Gradually, I became aware that I was lying in a heap in a mass of thick undergrowth, with the sunlight filtering through the leaves above me. My head ached intolerably and there was a dull pain at the back of my skull. My bush hat was still on my head, albeit somewhat battered and crushed, and as I dragged it off I felt it stick to my hair and scalp. Running my fingers over the back of my head I felt a sticky matted mass, and my fingers came away covered with half-congealed blood.

After a short time, my head began to clear, and it dawned upon me that I was lying at the foot of the embankment carrying the approach road to the bridge, below the spot where I had set up my firing position. I must have been hit on the back on the head as I crouched down after the explosion by something which had knocked me senseless; then I had rolled down the bank into the bushes at the bottom. My pack was still on my back, and my Sten gun lay beside me; that had been slung on my shoulder as I depressed the handle of the exploder.

I had no idea how long I had been there, but the sunlight shining through the leaves came from overhead, so it must have been for some considerable time.

I took a drink of water from my water bottle, and felt much better as a result, then, as the last traces of fog cleared from my brain, I proceeded to take stock of the situation. One thing stood out a mile. I was in an extremely desperate position. By this time the column would be miles away, in almost any direction, and I had little hope of catching them up, even if I had known their destination. A wave of depression swept over me, and I almost gave way to despair as I saw visions of a Japanese prison camp, or what was a great deal more probable, the business end of a long bayonet.

After a while, I controlled myself and started to think again. I had a Sten gun and four magazines, about eighty rounds of ammunition, and two grenades in the way of arms; three packets of K rations, sufficient food for three meals, and a water bottle. Apart from these articles, my pack contained only my Mae West—and to my surprise—the little brass Buddha. Blanket, ground sheet, spare clothing and the rest of my rations had been emptied out to make room for the explosives.

I examined the wound at the back of my head with a little more care, and I was relieved to find that I did not seem to be very seriously damaged. There was a large bump, and a fair sized gash: that was all. That was something at any rate on the credit side, but it did little to counterbalance the gloomy facts on the debit side. I was miles behind the Japanese lines, my companions had departed without having had time to miss me in the haste of their getaway, I had food for three meals only, and I was quite alone.

The leeches had been having a wonderful time during the period of my unconsciousness, and my face, neck and hands were smeared with blood and covered with numerous bites. That was a small matter however, and of no consequence, by comparison with my unenviable plight.

The sound of voices interrupted my gloomy thoughts, and I crouched down into the undergrowth. For one dreadful moment, I thought that I was discovered; as the owners of the voices began to descend the side of the embankment, my heart almost stood still as the awful vision of the long bayonet rose before my eyes again. The scrambling sound ceased as the men above me stopped, and I breathed again as they began to talk together. I could see nothing of them, and I dare not move, but I guessed that they were examining the exploder which had almost certainly been left behind.

Several minutes passed with the invisible men above me chattering away like excited parrots, and then suddenly an object came crashing through the foliage above me and landed by my side. To say that I started is to put it mildly. I almost jumped clean out of my skin. Nothing further happened. Then I heard them climb the bank, and their voices gradually died away as they moved off in the direction of the bridge. As soon as they had quite gone, I plucked up my courage and sat up, groping for the object which had so narrowly missed me. I picked it up and saw that it was an iron bolt about twelve inches in length, with some fragments of timber still clinging to the head. In a flash I realised that it was the missile which had knocked me senseless, a bolt from the bridge blown into the air by the explosion which had landed, of all places, on the back of my head. Evidently one of the Japs had seen it lying on the side of the embankment and had picked it up to examine it; having discovered that it was nothing but a fragment of debris from the bridge, he had simply flung it down the embankment, nearly to descend upon me once again.

This little incident impressed upon me that it was necessary for me to make myself scarce; at any time one of the enemy might stumble upon me as they searched the vicinity of the bridge. So I proceeded to crawl cautiously through the bushes away from the embankment, and by this means managed to regain the cover of the jungle where I felt moderately safe.

After thinking very seriously, I decided that I must try to get back to the Chindwin again, where, by some means or other, I might manage to make a crossing—a slim chance, but the only possible one. It seemed to me that the *chaung* was running in that direction; not that that was very much to rely upon in such broken country where rivers twisted and turned for miles in almost every direction. My silk map told me very little, and so I resolved to follow the bank of the *chaung* where the vegetation would be thinner, or at any rate some sort of a path would exist, and risk meeting Japanese or unfriendly villagers. Another consideration was that I could not last long on my own in the jungle. Apart from other dangers, which certainly existed, I should starve, whereas there would be fish in the river which I could catch with the aid of my two grenades, and I stood a chance of being able to buy food from the villages which would probably lie along the banks of the stream. I should mention that every officer was issued with twenty-five silver rupees; paper money was quite useless in a country flooded with worthless Jap paper money, and every man ten, for just such a purpose.

So I set off; I had hacked off my trouser button compass and I saw that I was heading roughly north-west. After a few minutes my curiosity got the better of my fears, and I cautiously approached the edge of the stream to catch a glimpse of the bridge. To my great satisfaction I saw that the demolition had been a complete success;

four of the piers were cut off at water level, three of the spans had completely disappeared below the surface of the water, and two others were half-submerged. A small group of Japanese officers standing at the gap in the bridge served to remind me of the plight that I was in, so I pushed on again.

I soon realised that there was a great deal of difference between travelling through the jungle alone and in the company of a large body of troops. The jungle was far from being the empty silent place that it had previously seemed. There were birds, although not as many as I should have imagined, and various small animals which crashed away through the undergrowth at my approach, and I saw my first snake, a hideous slim, green thing wrapped round a trailing vine. I realised only too well then that tramping in the forest means sliding, scrambling, pulling at the vines and thorns which catch at the clothing, tearing hands on the cutting grasses, becoming mixed up in sticky spiders' webs, being bitten by ants and flies, until one is swollen, harassed, exhausted, bleeding—and above all frightened, as I was, so that one can never be sure that that cold, wet vine that clings to one's neck, or trails across the back of the hand, is not that mortally poisonous snake that one has been dreading for so long.

I struggled on along the bank of the *chaung*, slipping, sliding, and scrambling through the tangled bushes until the declining sun told me that the day was drawing to a close and I must seek a resting place for the night. I had eaten a portion of one K ration as I walked, but I was still very hungry. Since there was nothing that I could do about this, I drank as much water as I could in an attempt to relieve the pangs of hunger, but with little success. Although the sun had not then disappeared below the surrounding hills, the comparative silence of the jungle was already broken by the stirring of its countless unseen inhabitants; an occasional rustle close at hand made me start, as also did the barking of a wild dog, and an unearthly howl, perhaps from a hyena, in the distance filled me with trepidation. An awful sense of isolation and utter helplessness came over me, and my fears almost turned to panic as the always dim light of the jungle began to fade, and my imagination painted vivid pictures of snakes and ravenous wild animals lurking all around me, waiting only for the fall of darkness before they pounced upon me. I dare not build a bed of bamboo as I had done with the column, for then there had been safety in numbers; whereas I was utterly alone. For some time I was at a loss, and the feeling of despair, never very far away, threatened to overwhelm me completely.

At length I came upon a tall, flat-topped rock at the edge of the *chaung*, and decided that if I climbed to the top, which I did with some difficulty, I should be fairly safe from anything which might come out of jungle or river. Nothing could come upon me without making a noise, and I had my loaded Sten gun by my side. I blew up the Mae West for a pillow, and laid myself down.

It was still light out there in the open, and, after a few minutes, I sat up and looked about me, seeing for the first time what had been before my eyes during the whole of the day. All day it had been the same; the *chaung* winding and twisting in every direction, the wild hills all around closing in and then receding again, and the gloomy green jungle stretching on and on with never a break. There was beauty, wild and untamed, in that remote *chaung*, set like some gleaming jewel between the sombre walls of green, its rippling surface flashing blue and gold from the reflected light of the setting sun and the deep blue sky overhead, the spits and banks of yellow sand, and the smooth grey water-worn rocks breaking the expanse of the surface and dividing the fast flowing water into countless gurgling, bubbling channels; here and there a pool appeared, black and smooth, the encircling rocks moss grown, and the surrounding vegetation, broken by an occasional flash of gaudy colour, dark and green. A great feeling of insignificance came over me, a lonely human being amidst the wild grandeur of the unconquered hills.

Darkness descended rapidly and, with the light, the wild loveliness of the place faded away, and in its place there came a solemn sinister blackness filled with the hum and buzz of insects and the cries of creatures of the night. The very gurgle of the water seemed to change its tone and increase in volume until it became a steady rushing noise. I became terribly afraid—afraid of everything—the loneliness, the unseen denizens of the jungle and, above all, of the unknown—that strange inexplicable fear that I had not experienced since the days of my childhood. I buried my head inside my pack and stuffed my hands in my pockets, partly as a protection against mosquitoes, but principally for the same reason that makes an ostrich bury its head in the sand at the approach of danger. It began to grow chilly, and I huddled up in an effort at keeping warm, for I sorely missed my blanket. For a long time I could not, I dare not, sleep, and I lay thinking gloomy thoughts with the harsh croak of the bull frogs, and the rasping chirp of the cicadas sounding in my ears. Eventually weariness overcame me and I fell asleep.

I was awake again as soon as it was light, feeling very much better and, after finishing the remainder of the K ration for my breakfast, I proceeded to lay in a stock of rations for the journey. I selected a pool connected to the stream by a narrow opening, in which I thought I should find some fish. Taking a grenade from my pocket, I removed the pin and threw it into the centre of the pool. After the usual five seconds had elapsed, there was a muffled explosion and a column of water rose from the surface. Nothing happened and I began to think that I had wasted a grenade; but I was too impatient and soon quite a number of fish came floating, belly uppermost to the surface of the water. These I dragged to the edge of the pool with a long piece of bamboo, and straightaway fell to hacking them into slices with my jack knife. Next I moved well into the jungle, where I hoped the trees would disperse the smoke, and lighted a fire of dry bamboo. I held the pieces of fish on a sliver of bamboo over this fire and half-smoked and half-scorched them. The result was not of a particularly appetising appearance, but I knew that it would keep for some time and should at least prevent me from starving.

I have mentioned earlier that I had received no adequate training in jungle lore; I only learned afterwards that a meagre subsistence might be gleaned from the jungle itself, that certain berries and fruits were edible, that the heart of a palm tree, the tuft of young leaves at the crown somewhat resembles cabbage, that even young bamboo shoots will help to keep a desperate man from starving. Had I known these things, it is possible that I might not have chosen fish, and then—but all that I suppose is idle supposition.

Having packed my rations into my pack, I started on my journey once again. The going was very difficult; the undergrowth was thick, and the ground beneath my feet alternated between irregular rocks and patches of sticky mud. As I stumbled on I wondered with a grim feeling of humour, what my Mother would think if she could see me. I am quite sure that she would not have recognised the muddy, unwashed scarecrow that I was, as her son, bearing so little resemblance to the smartly tailored officer with whom she was familiar.

So the day passed as I wandered on and on along the bank of the winding *chaung*, until weariness overcame me; then, as it was drawing towards evening, I sought out another resting place for the night, finally deciding upon the crook of the limb of a large tree, in default of a convenient rock. I fell asleep haunted by fears of snakes, and spent a most uncomfortable night, filled with unpleasant dreams, and bruised by the gnarled trunk of the tree.

The following morning found me unbitten by snakes, but very much bitten by mosquitoes; and having made my breakfast upon some of the dried fish and a fragment of K ration, I started off again. I had not been travelling for very long when I felt a sudden violent pain in the pit of my stomach which made me gasp for breath; it passed, but soon returned, and then I was violently sick. The sickness left me weak and shaking and indescribably miserable with the former feeling of utter despair again creeping over me. I had no idea what was the cause of the sickness; perhaps it was the fish, or even the first symptoms of some ghastly tropical disease; but I did know that, unless it passed off, I could not travel very much further.

It did not pass off. At times during the day waves of nausea swept over me, and the muddy ground beneath my feet seemed to heave and roll like the flank of some mighty living creature, and the light of day grew dim before my eyes. Then it would pass and, as my physical distress eased, so did the pangs of real terror grip me. The grim hostility of the jungle pressed heavily upon me and I began to imagine that I could see Jap soldiers grinning at me from behind every tree and bush. The very jungle itself seemed to ferment, to pulsate with an evil life all of its own, and I wanted to scream, to run in a panic—away from the brooding forces of Evil about me.

By the late afternoon I could scarcely crawl along, quite sure in my own mind that I had reached the end of my tether. For some time I had been stumbling along a rough path, although I had scarcely been aware of it in my distress of body and mind, when, without any warning, I rounded a bend in the path and came upon a clearing with a village in the centre. I was now too far gone to worry about Japanese or unfriendly villagers, and so I staggered towards the bamboo huts. I was soon spotted by some children and, after they had raised the alarm, a little crowd of men, women and children came to meet me. With my strange dishevelled appearance they must have thought that I was some sort of a devil coming out of the jungle; yet they approached me cautiously, and, seeing that I was but a man, and a sick one, they plucked up courage and surrounded me, asking me questions. I understood not a single word and could only mutter:

"British soldier. Very sick," or something like that.

Someone amongst them seemed to understand; then I was half led, and half carried into the village and taken into one of the huts where I collapsed completely as a wave of blackness and nausea swept over me. An absolute nightmare of vomiting and violent pains followed, with long periods of merciful unconsciousness between, which must have lasted all night, for it was morning before I began to feel better, though dreadfully weak.

I had been left alone for some time and, having recovered sufficiently to take interest in my surroundings, I sat up and looked around me. The hut was small; constructed of bamboo with a thatched roof and a hard, almost polished, floor of trampled earth; it was very clean and scantily furnished, containing nothing but the bed upon which I lay, a bamboo table and chair, a small tin box and a few utensils. A folded mosquito net above my head attracted my attention; a very unusual article in such a remote and primitive village!

A noise from the direction of the door made me turn my head in that direction, and there I saw an extremely pleasant looking Burmese girl approaching me. She was small and slight, with a fair, almost white, complexion, and glossily black hair tied in a loose knot at the nape of her neck, with a band of coloured artificial flowers to one side of her forehead. She was dressed in an ankle length *lungyi* of brightly-patterned material, and a flimsy blouse of white muslin worn over the top of a very tight white bodice. Her wooden sandals made a little irregular clicking noise as she walked across the hard floor, to stand by the side of the bed smiling at me. She was the first Burmese girl that I had ever seen and, in her gay clothes, she made a very attractive picture, as she stood by my side smiling down at me. My pleasure was greatly enhanced when she spoke to me—in English.

"You are feeling better now?"

"Yes thank you," I replied, "I am far better than I ever thought to be again. I scarcely expected that I would find myself in such friendly hands. But where am I?"

She made some unintelligible reply; then giving me a last sweet smile she hurried from the hut, to return a few minutes later with a bowl of rice and some water. To my surprise I felt well enough to eat; indeed I was quite hungry. As I dealt with the food, eating it with my fingers, she sat by my side, saying very little, but smiling all the time. As soon as I had finished, she left the hut again and came back with a man, clearly a barber, for he carried a little shaving pot and brush and an open cut-throat razor. Without a word, he set to work and proceeded to shave me. After he had finished, the girl brought me water in an earthenware vessel and a clean *lungyi*: then, telling me to undress, she left the hut. I washed myself and donned the *lungyi,* experiencing some difficulty in fixing the unfamiliar garment around my waist, and my clothes were taken away by a solemn brown-faced little boy with a shaven head, and returned a few hours later washed and ironed.

The effect of all this upon my morale may be imagined; the hovering feeling of despair left me completely and I felt almost cheerful, facing the future with something like confidence at this unexpected turn in the trend of events.

After a time the girl came back accompanied by an elderly Burman, wearing the usual *lungyi* and a shirt,with a coloured piece of cloth twisted around his head, radiating an air of importance and displaying an arm band marked with Burmese characters. Under his right arm he carried a large double-barrelled shotgun—a rather ominous touch, I thought.

"This is the headman," she said. "He does not speak English, but I can tell you what he says. He hopes that you are well and he would like to know how you got here, and if it means that the British are coming back again?"

My descent to earth, started by the sight of the shotgun, was completed suddenly. I remembered what I had been told—that, whilst many of the villagers were friendly, some of them were in the pay of the Japanese, or else Japanese sympathisers. This might be but the prelude to handing me over to the Japanese—perhaps the enemy were already on their way to collect me. Once again my spirits found a resting place within my boots.

I thought rapidly. I could do no harm by saying that I was a member of a raiding party; the enemy were only too well aware of the presence of that raiding party!

"Yes I am well again," I answered, "and I am very grateful for the kind treatment which has been given to me. I belonged to a party of British troops who are in the area, but I became lost. I can tell you quite definitely that the British are coming back again—soon."

The girl translated what I said, and he appeared to be satisfied for his solemn face broke into a grin and, after talking to her for a few minutes, he gravely inclined his head and left the hut. In a few moments he came back—and to my great surprise he was carrying the little brass Buddha in his hand. He gave it to me and I accepted it mechanically as he began to speak. The girl translated, and it appeared that he was telling me that he had been looking after it for me, whilst I was ill, that it would be several days before he could carry out all the instructions, and in the meantime I must make myself as comfortable as I could. It left me completely in the dark, but some instinct warned me to remain silent; I said nothing, merely nodding my head to all that he said. Bowing slightly he left the hut, leaving the girl and I alone.

She looked at me curiously for some moments, and then asked me a question which suprised me.

"Are you really a British soldier?"

I was so astonished that for some seconds I could only stand and stare at her.

"Yes of course I am," I finally managed to reply. "What else could I be? In fact I am a British officer."

"Then what is that thing that you have there, and how did you get it?" she answered, pointing to the Buddha.

It began to dawn upon me that there was more to the little image than was at first apparent; but for the life of me I could not tell what it was. After thinking for a few moments, I took the plunge, telling her that I had obtained it by accident, that I knew nothing of its origin, or what it was, beyond being a badly-made statue of Buddha.

It was her turn to look surprised as she said:

"If I were you, I would not tell that to anyone else. I know nothing about it, but the headman has said that it is very important, and that you are to be well looked after because of it; but for that I am sure that he would not dare to allow you to remain here: he is very much afraid of the Japanese, and sometimes they come here."

I was completely bewildered by all this, but said very little, thinking that would be the wisest course to adopt until I knew just a little more about the matter.

After she left the hut I lay thinking about it, trying to read a meaning into the cryptic remarks uttered by the headman, wondering if the mystery was nothing but a figment of my imagination, looking at the matter from every angle, and turning over in my mind the events which had led to the statuette falling into my hands; but nothing would crystallise and eventually I fell asleep.

I saw her from time to time during the next day or so, and I was gratified to find that she still appeared to be friendly and even helpful. I talked to her as much as I was able and managed to get her to tell me how she came to be in that village.

"You see I am not of these people at all," she said. "I am a Karen from Toungoo in the south, and I have lived here for about eighteen months. I am not even a Buddhist as these people are. I am a Christian, and I was educated at a Christian girls' school in Rangoon, and lived there after I left the school. I was a companion and a nurse to the lady of an English family in the city. When the Japanese came they left Rangoon and fled north, and I came with them. We had a dreadful time, there was much bombing and machine gunning, and we travelled as far as we could until there was no more petrol; then we had to walk. We travelled with a large party of other refugees and crossed the Irrawaddy by country boat. Soon after that cholera broke out amongst us, and very many people died. My lady became ill, and both of the children as well, so we could not travel any more. They died one by one, and then the Englishman killed himself with a pistol that he carried; and I was left alone.

"I stayed with the people of a nearby village until the Japanese came nearer, then I came further into the jungle to this village. I am welcome here because I have been trained as a nurse, and I do much to help the people. You would not have liked to have lived in any of the other huts; they are dirty, and the people are very ignorant; and you were ill and only I could look after you."

Her name was Ma Pu, but she said:

"Call me Mary, for that is my name also. I have a Burmese name, a Karen name, and an English name."

"Whatever you do you must look after the Buddha," she said finally. "I can see that it is not really a Buddha at all, for the right hand and arm should be stretched down, and the left arm bent across the front of the body with the palm of the hand uppermost. The writing on the bottom looks like Japanese, but I don't know what it means. I think that the headman is going to send for the Japanese; but I don't think that you need be afraid, for he has told me that you are a very important person to them."

I am afraid that her assurances did little to quieten my fears. It was all too fantastic for words. Why should I be an important person? What did the Buddha mean? It must all be some sort of a dream.

BURMESE VILLAGE

THE next two or three days passed very pleasantly as I began to recover my strength and feel myself once again, and I could have wished that it might have gone on for ever. I spent the days watching the women and children in the village, and talking, through the medium of Mary as interpreter, with the greybeards of the village. I tried to put over a line of propaganda to them, not forgetting that I was in some way supposed to be connected with the Japanese, painting pictures of the might of the British land, sea and air forces, and telling them over and over again that assuredly one day the white men would come back.

I soon realised the truth of what Mary had said about the other people in the village having habits that would not endear them to me. They were very primitive in that out-of-the-way spot, although in advance of many of the Indian villagers that I have met. The women were quite unlike Mary; their skin was darker in colour, their hair unkempt and greasy; indeed one of their favourite occupations seemed to be examining each others' heads for vermin, often squatting down in a line, one behind the other for that purpose in the dust outside their huts. They appeared to have little modesty, for they commonly wore just a rather dirty *lungyi* fastened above their breasts, which seemed to need constant adjustment, being frequently unfastened and lowered to reveal the whole of the upper part of their bodies before being pulled tight again. They were equally careless when washing themselves at the edge of the stream. In common with many other Eastern people, they washed, wearing their usual garment the *lungyi*, so that the garment was washed at the same time as themselves. Having finished they would step into another dry *lungyi*, pull it above their waists, and then drop the wet garment before tightening the dry *lungyi* about themselves; thus, in theory, not revealing any private part of their bodies to the public gaze. In fact, however, they were very careless, and on one occasion a rather portly lady dropped her wet garment before donning the dry one, by accident of course, and stood before me for several seconds quite naked; whilst she leisurely retrieved the fallen garment, favouring me with a saucy grin as she caught sight of my astonished expression.

Many of the women wore ornaments in their ears made of what appeared to be amber, but which was probably some gum-like substance of local origin. They were enormous things in the shape of a cone, very much elongated, one fastened on each side of the lobe of each ear; which had the effect of twisting the lower part of their ears at right angles to their heads.

The men appeared to do very little work, a common thing in Burma, whilst the women worked all day long; yet strangely enough there was no sign of the sex inequality so strongly marked in India. Indeed on several occasions I observed a lady dealing her husband a resounding buffet upon the ear as a punishment for some sin of omission or commission.

One morning, the sight of the villagers collecting their poultry and taking it away from the village, told me that something different was about to happen. I waited as calmly as I could, but not without severe misgivings and wild thoughts of taking to my heels. I had not long to wait; and, at about ten o'clock in the morning, I saw in the distance along the bank of the *chaung* in the direction opposite to that from which I had come, a small body of men marching towards the village.

As they came nearer I saw that they were twelve in number; with an officer at the head stepping along very stiffly, his men trailing behind in a ragged, slovenly formation. They were dressed in the usual drab Japanese uniform; long, loose tunic with two patch pockets set somewhere between breast and waist, knee breeches with long puttees, and their curious canvas and rubber boots having a separate compartment for the big toe. They all wore leather equipment and carried the long, old-fashioned-looking, Japanese rifle. The officer was dressed in a similar manner, but his uniform was of better cut and material, and he wore polished riding boots instead of puttees, and a long sword hung from his Sam Browne belt. They all wore the same tall, floppy caps with a little peak at the front. From the badges of rank on the officer's collar, a golden patch with two red bands and three stars, I saw that he was a Captain.

They marched into the centre of the village and halted. I observed the proceedings from the door of a hut, waiting with the Buddha in my hand, realising, by this time, that it was the key to the whole business. At a sharp word from one of the soldiers, the headman approached the officer, and salaamed in obvious fear and respect. A brief conversation followed, which ended with the headman leading the way to the hut where I waited, I confess, with my knees knocking together with very strong misgivings as to the outcome of it all. Somehow or other, I suppressed the more obvious signs of my fear, and managed to put on a bold front by leaving the doorway of the hut and walking to meet them.

Immediately I appeared the officer stopped dead, his narrow eyes narrowing even more, his hand straying to the butt of a pistol in a leather holster at his side, whilst the men behind him broke into an excited chatter. It was very obvious that they had not expected to see a white man in the uniform of a British soldier. He barked a sharp word to his men, and immediately I was surrounded by a ring of menacing bayonets, and once again my heart sank.

He turned to the headman who had been following at his heels and began to question him in a loud and angry voice, slapping his face the while to add emphasis to his words. The unfortunate man howled for mercy, almost grovelling on the ground, and I caught the words '*Buddha Thakin*' and I knew that he was trying to draw attention to the little statuette. I took my cue from this and brandished the Buddha in the air. It had an immediate effect, and the Jap captain began to bark questions at me, instead of at the badly-frightened headman; but without any form of physical persuasion, a sign that I was of some importance, surprising as it was. However I understood not a word, and none of the Japanese could speak English. In the end he took the Buddha from me and examined it carefully. A change of expression came over his face, and he ordered his men to lower their bayonets. As the menacing points were lowered, my faith in the little statuette rose considerably; clearly there was something about it.

After an ineffectual attempt at making me understand what he was saying, he signed to me to accompany him and I, perforce, complied. We marched off in a little bunch with myself in the centre, which showed quite clearly that, although I was for some reason privileged, I was still a prisoner.

Soon the village in the little clearing was left behind, and we were moving along a rough track leading through the jungle. The ground was rough and uneven and I began to feel very hot and breathless, an indication that I was still suffering from the effects of my illness. However

I managed to keep moving, and after walking about five miles we came upon another, wider track where a motor vehicle stood waiting. It was one of the ordinary Japanese vehicles with which I was later to become familiar, a blunt-nosed vehicle reminiscent of a Chevrolet. Into the back of this we all piled, with the exception of the officer who sat by the driver, and bounced off along the track at a good pace.

We travelled along bumpy tracks and earth roads for about three hours, and then came upon a much wider road with a fair amount of traffic on it. After about another hour we arrived at the entrance to a large camp; a headquarters of some description I imagined. I was taken into a large bamboo *basha*, and left with two of the soldiers to act as a guard. These two men were disposed to be friendly and grinned at me; however the language difficulty prevented any 'fraternisation', and in any case I was not in a talkative mood. I was racking my brains in an attempt at thinking out a plan of action. It was all very difficult, but somehow or other it appeared that the possession of the statuette turned me into a person of some importance. I still had it in my possession for the officer handed it back to me before we left the village; that also had surprised me. I could think of no satisfactory explanation. I could only resolve to try to make someone betray the meaning of the Buddha by pretending that I knew all about it.

I had not long to ponder the matter, for the officer reappeared, and signed for me to follow him. I did as I was bid, and we passed through the camp with many curious eyes upon me, and came to a long low building of a more substantial nature than the others in the camp. We entered the building and I found myself in a fairly well-furnished room with a large desk at one end, behind sat a bespectacled and portly Japanese, wearing the badges of rank of a Colonel. At his side stood another Japanese officer. As I entered the room I actually saw an expression of utter amazement appear on their faces. I was, very obviously, not what they had expected to see. For some moments there was silence followed by a rapid exchange of Japanese, then the Captain, for that was his rank, who stood by the desk said, with the broadest possible American accent:

"You have the stachew of Buddha?"

I handed it over to them and they examined it with great care. It appeared to satisfy them, for they handed it back to me—again to my surprise—and he said:

"We are sure surprised to see you. We did not know who would bring the information but I guess we never expected to see an Englishman. We were kinda suspicious of you at the beginning, but you've got the Buddha so I guess you're the man."

I suppose that it was the word 'information' that gave me my cue; anyway I realised in a flash that I was the bearer of some piece of important information in the shape of the little brass Buddha, incredible as it seemed. Evidently it had been handed to the Burmese private by the Indian civilian who was in the pay of the Japanese, to be brought into Burma and handed over to the enemy. The Japanese then must have had some knowledge that a second Wingate expedition was being prepared. Or perhaps only their agent had been aware of this fact and he was using the Burman, or had intended to do so, to bring this information to the notice of the Japanese. But why the Buddha? It just did not make sense. How could a little brass image be of any significance?

A sudden impulse made me decide to try a spot of bluff.

"But I am not an Englishman," I replied. "I am a Eurasian. My father was a Frenchman, and my mother was a Kashmiri woman, and I have many reasons for hating the British."

"Then how did you come to be British Army, and how did you get to Burma?"

"I joined the Royal Army Medical Corps as a Medical Orderly, but I have been so badly treated, and sneered at because I am a half-breed that I've come to hate them all. I had no choice about coming into Burma. I just had to come as a member of a raiding party. I was given the Buddha at Manipur Road station to bring with me into Burma, with instructions to leave my own unit and report to the nearest Japanese Army unit as soon as I could."

"How long you been workin' for us?" was his next question.

"For a few months only," I replied, wondering how soon it would be before I tripped myself up with my wild inventions.

Then came the question that I had been dreading.

"Tell us all you know about this raiding party. Who are they? How many? Where are they now?

I dare not hesitate for fear of arousing suspicion; yet I had to be very careful or I should assuredly betray my comrades. By pretending to be a Medical Orderly, a non-combatant O.R., I thought that I could safely feign a good deal of ignorance.

"They are British Infantry," I replied. "And there are about two hundred of them, (a grossly inaccurate figure). I can't say where they are now, since I have been away from them for many days."

"What arms do they carry?"

"Rifles and automatic weapons," I replied.

So the grilling went on, and I was asked every conceivable question. My brain was in a turmoil as I told lie after lie, twisting, turning, evading, and striving only to reveal information with which the Japs must already have been familiar. God knows if I gave anything away. I was tortured by fear that I had done so for a long time afterwards, but I think now that, if I did let anything slip, it was very little, and of no particular value. In any case I am sure that the lies that I told caused some confusion at any rate. I elaborated the statement that I was a Eurasian with a bitter grudge against everything British for all I was worth; and in this I was helped by my dark complexion, and because I speak French quite well. I told stories of high-handed treatment meted out to me by British civilians in India, which had aroused my bitterness to such an extent that I was prepared to do anything to bring about their downfall. I even said that I lived in Chandernagore, the French Colony near to Calcutta, where, I alleged, my father had been a minor French official. I have thought since that I was skating on very thin ice when I made this statement; I had never even been to the place, and, if my questioners had been at all familiar with that part of India, I should have been exposed immediately. Yet somehow or other I got away with it. I can't think how I managed to lie so convincingly; perhaps it was because I realised that my life depended upon it; but it was principally because I hit upon the idea of masquerading as an embittered French Indian, I am sure, and the ignorance on the part of the Japanese of the working of the European mind. I am perfectly certain that I could never have got away with such a cock and bull yarn if I had been in the hands of the Germans.

I must have been grilled for a good hour, although I did not realise it at the time, so occupied was my brain with desperate mental gymnastics. I only know that, when the interview finally came to an end, and I was taken away and left alone in a *basha* with a guard outside the door—what chance had I of escape anyway—a terrific reaction set in, and I collapsed on the ground in a trembling heap. I had suffered before, but this hell of fear and doubt almost drove me mad. I was afraid for my own precious skin, afraid of the consequences of what I had done and said, and above all that I had betrayed my own comrades. Perhaps it was a trick, and the Japanese were only leading me on, pretending to believe my stories so that they could worm all that I knew out of me, and soon they would kill me. Even if they did believe me where was the end to this thing? Should I not be guilty of high treason by adhering to the enemy, and be shot, if ever I returned to my own country? Round and round it went in my brain until I felt like screaming.

It was well that I had been left alone or I must have betrayed myself by such an exhibition of terror and remorse. I have no idea how long I was in such a condition, but I do hope that I may never again have to grapple with such a state of mind and conscience as I did then. I am powerless to describe my real feelings, they were too horrible for any words of mine.

At length I brought myself to a slightly happier frame of mind by realising that I was at least alive, and well treated—purely selfish considerations as they may be, but they were enough to restore my sanity when, God knows, I needed to keep my wits about me.

My meals, such as they were, were brought to me by a grinning Japanese soldier who appeared to fancy his command of the English language. Every time he entered the hut, he greeted me with a string of meaningless words. It was quite obvious that he had no idea of their meaning from the parrot-like fashion with which he repeated them, yet it appeared to give him a considerable amount of satisfaction, and I have no doubt that he told many tales to his admiring comrades of his dealings with the queer individual he was looking after. His usual greeting was: "Is that you Sergeant Smith?" or occasionally: "Come and help me I am wounded," and once or twice: "Thik hai Johnny." It sounded so utterly ridiculous until I realised that, if I heard those self-same words on a pitch-black night in the jungle when the Japanese jitter parties were out, striving to make me incautiously reveal my position, or be inveigled into going to help 'Sergeant Smith', it would be nerve-racking rather than ridiculous. They were a sample of the few words of English taught to the Japanese for just that purpose.

I was in that camp for little more than twenty-four hours, and most of that time was spent inside the hut. After I had overcome my mental distress, I took an interest in everything, making mental notes of all that I saw for future reference. The Japanese soldiers appeared to lounge about all day with little in the way of training to keep them occupied; yet discipline was severe, and I saw many face-smacking incidents. I was soon to learn that this was the common form of reprimand and correction, for a wide variety of minor offences. If a soldier did anything to displease his officer, his face was slapped vigorously there and then, and he did not appear to resent it. This should be borne in mind when reading accounts of the indignities to which Europeans in the hands of the Japanese were subjected; it may be an indignity to a European for his face to be smacked, but it is certainly not so to a Japanese who expects that punishment.

I also caught a glimpse of some highly decorative females who lived near to the Jap officers' quarters; they were probably the Commander's own ladies who helped him to beguile away the lonely evenings.

Transport was definitely short; nearly all the vehicles were of the same pattern as the one in which I had travelled a little earlier, and bullock carts were used to a large extent. The senior officers had ordinary private cars for their use; cars which had probably been left behind by evacuees in 1942.

On the day following my arrival at the camp, I was taken before the English speaking officer, and informed that I was going to Rangoon at once with my information. A vehicle was waiting to take me to the airstrip, and I should fly from there.

All this was even more amazing. An incredible amount of importance appeared to be attached to the statuette, and I was actually given a leather valise to carry it in, with strict instructions not to part company with it until I reached Rangoon under any consideration. My feelings may be fairly described as being mixed. It was clear that I was being accepted at face value, whatever that was, and my incredible story had been swallowed wholesale; but at the same time I was going deeper into enemy occupied territory, to the very centre of the net, and I just could not imagine what the outcome of it all would be.

I had little time to consider these points for I was taken outside, and introduced to another Japanese Captain who was waiting with a large Ford saloon car. He was to be my escort during the journey. I was pleased to find that he spoke a little English; he had probably been selected for that reason, and I hoped that I might be able to extract a little information from him before we reached Rangoon which would help to prepare me for what was waiting there.

At first he was very stiff and correct, obviously considering a traitor B.O.R. beneath his dignity. Did I not bless the unknown British officer, probably Wingate himself, who had decided that no badges of rank should be worn on the expedition, and no papers carried which would give the slightest clue to the rank of any individual. I am quite sure that I should not have got away with it, if it had been known that I was an officer. I was rather amused at his attempts to be dignified and distant, because his curiosity was obviously aroused, and he was itching to ask me questions. At length his curiosity got the better of him and he gave it up as a bad job and became friendly. He started off by asking me who I was.

"An important messenger," I replied.

He was suitably impressed, and asked many more questions, relevant and otherwise.

"How you come?"

"I came with a British raiding party."

"Ah! They make bridge break; very bad."

I disclaimed all knowledge of the 'broken bridge', but I was glad to learn that my comrades were regarded as being very bad; evidently the attack upon the bridge had caused quite a stir. He appeared to know very little, and I got little out of him despite my judicious pumping, as I answered his questions. He only knew that he was taking me to Rangoon because I carried important information, but he did mention the name of Babu Singh as if he expected me to know someone of that name. I pretended to understand what he was talking about but naturally it meant nothing to me. Of the Buddha itself he knew absolutely nothing. He asked to see it in the end, and I obligingly produced it from the leather valise. He took it from me very carefully and handled it, as though it was fragile, turning it over and over with great care for some moments, and then returning it to me with the remark:

"Him open eh?"

That was something that had not occurred to me before, but now he had mentioned it, it did seem to be quite possible. What other meaning could it have? It must contain something, but if it did I could not imagine what that something could be; furthermore from its weight it appeared to be solid, and I could discover no sign of an opening, even though I examined it very carefully.

I gave him the impression that it did open, and that satisfied him. After that we fell silent; any sort of conversation being something of a strain upon my companion's limited English vocabulary, and I fell to pondering this new possibility. The more I thought about it, the more credible it became, principally because it seemed to be the only possible explanation of the whole mystery. If it contained information of some sort I just could not guess what that information could be, or in what form it existed, and I could not understand why such a curious method of transmitting information should have been adopted in these days of efficient wireless telegraphy—it was too reminiscent of a wildly improbable 'thriller'. In the end I had to leave the problem unsolved, and turned my attention to the country through which we were passing.

The road was fairly good and we bowled along rapidly, passing several camps, and a large Ordnance dump. Most of the vehicles on the road were the usual blunt-nosed three-tonners, with a sprinkling of requisitioned civilian and captured British vehicles. Once we passed a tankette rocking along at a good pace, raising clouds of dust from the dry earth road—it had not rained very much since we crossed the Chindwin. The country was still hilly and jungle-clad, little different from the country through which I had passed with the column.

After travelling for about six or seven miles we arrived at the airstrip. It certainly did not earn the title of airfield, being nothing more than a stretch of paddy field with the bunds flattened, set at the bottom of a broad valley. It did not exceed a thousand yards in length, and had no surfacing of any description, so it could only be a fair weather strip. Only a few planes were visible, and they were well dispersed. This dispersal, together with the sight of a few unfilled bomb craters, showed that the place occasionally received a little attention from the R.A.F. We were stopped by a sentry, as we turned off the road, and directed to a long *basha* standing beneath the cover afforded by a group of trees, where we found a group of Japanese pilots whiling away the time with a card game of some sort. A brief conversation ensued, my escort brushing aside the questions which were showered upon him, and I found myself again the centre of interest. Meanwhile one of the pilots began to prepare himself for the flight, buckling a leather helmet on to his head, and climbing into a suit of overalls; finally, to my astonishment, strapping a sword about his waist. I knew that every Japanese officer always carried a sword, but I had not realised that they carried the fetish to the absurd extent of wearing one in the narrow confines of an aeroplane cockpit.

As soon as he was ready, we walked to the plane which I eyed with interest. It was a twin-engined aircraft, rather like a Messerschmidt 110 in appearance, with radial engines, a twin-finned tail, and a long 'glass house' on the upper part of the fuselage. The usual Japanese markings were painted on the wings: two plain red circles, one on each wing tip, and the rest of the plane painted a grey-green colour. A ground crew was gathered about it; one of them slid back the sliding portion of the 'glass house' and we all climbed in. We sat in line with the pilot in the front, myself in the centre, and my escort behind in what was the air-gunner's seat. The engines were fitted with impulse starters, and I could see some of the ground crew winding away at a handle fitted into the engine nacelles for some time before the engines sprang into life, one after the other. A few moments afterwards we were bouncing across the uneven paddy, and were air-borne.

We flew for some hours, during the greater part of which time I was shivering with cold, clad as I was in thin jungle green, until at length I saw the broad gleaming band of a big river beneath us, which I guessed was the Irrawaddy, not far from Mandalay.

INDIAN NATIONAL ARMY

THE Irrawaddy was soon left behind; and, as we flew on, the country levelled out, and the border hills sank below the horizon, although some could still be seen out towards the east. The character of the countryside also changed, and we were flying over the dry, almost barren countryside of Central Burma, in marked contrast to the green jungle country in the north.

We landed at an airfield, which I learned was one of the Meiktila group of fields, to refuel, and we took off again soon afterwards, having stayed only to partake of a little refreshment. Once again I was the object of a great deal of interest, and once again my escort was subjected to a battery of questions, but he evaded most of them again. I imagine that he had been given definite instructions not to talk.

So we flew on heading steadily southwards, passing over towns and villages, following the railway where it runs along the valley of the Sittang; and then turning south-south-west in the direction of Rangoon, to fly over the great rice-producing area, mile after mile of flat paddy fields, yellow-brown after the gathering of the rice harvest.

It was late afternoon when we arrived at the end of our journey, and I caught a glimpse of the streets and houses of the city of Rangoon, dominated by the golden spire of the Schwe Dagon Pagoda, as we circled over the Mingaladon airfield north of the city. In a few minutes we were rolling over the smooth tarmac runway, and came to a halt in front of a roofless, burnt-out hangar. I climbed stiffly from the aircraft and looked about me with interest. A number of aircraft of various types were parked around the field, and glimpses of others standing behind blast walls of earth could be seen. There were Zero fighters, and '91' bombers, as well as a number of transport aircraft. I was given little opportunity to make a detailed study of the airfield, for our arrival had apparently been expected, and I was led behind the hangar where a closed car was waiting. We climbed in and drove away from the airfield.

The airfield is some distance, about ten miles, from Rangoon, and as we drove along I had time both to look about me and consider what I should do and say next. The outskirts of the city were really beautiful and well-planned, with many large European style houses standing in their own grounds. The Victoria Lakes in particular impressed me, a large irregular expanse of water with trees growing down to the waters edge, dotted with the white sails of little yachts. I could easily have imagined myself driving through the suburbs of an English town, instead of being in the peculiar predicament in which I found myself. The road was wide and well-surfaced, and the car moved at a good speed bearing me on to, I knew not what.

It was impossible for me to formulate any particular line of action beyond trying to live and act as Maurice Derocque, No. 5895643, of the Royal Army Medical Corps. I had decided upon this name and number earlier on, and had very carefully memorised it, along with a number of other details which I had worked out connected with this fictitious personality, realising that a contradiction in my statements might prove to be fatal. I was born in Chandernagore, French Indian territory, on the 26th February 1920 (my actual birthday) and I was the son of Jean Derocque, a Frenchman, and Bina

Derocque, a Kashmiri woman. A large part of my childhood had been spent in the north of France with my grandparents, (an area with which I was actually quite familiar), and I had not returned to India until I was nineteen years of age, to take up employment in a clerical position on the East Indian Railways. In 1942 I volunteered for service in the R.A.M.C., but my Army career had been an unhappy one, particularly after I was posted to a British unit where I was treated by the other men in a manner which had aroused my bitterness. Finally I went absent without leave, and, being absent for more than twenty-one days, I was posted as a deserter; the period of detention I served, after being apprehended, had intensified this feeling of bitterness to such a degree that I was prepared to do anything. A little while after my release from detention I was contacted in Calcutta by a man, unknown to me, who promised me a large sum of money if I would act as a messenger on an operation in which he had reason to believe I would soon be taking part. After some persuasion I agreed, and accepted the sum of Rs.2,500, with the promise of twice that sum if I carried out instructions. It was pointed out to me that I should run little risk, in fact would probably be evading danger, whilst I stood to gain a great deal besides doing the hated British a disservice, and getting myself out of the Army. Eventually I was given instructions to contact an employee of the Bengal and Assam Railways when I passed through Manipur Road Railway Station, and receive an object which I was to take with me to pass on to the Japanese at the earliest opportunity; the object being of such a nature that it could not possibly arouse suspicion. I should make myself known by standing on the engine's rear platform wearing a shirt with the top button hooked in the second button hole. An Indian would approach me and ask me if I was looking for a bookstall. All this had happened, and an Indian civilian wearing a blue shirt had handed the little Buddha to me. I brought it with me as instructed, and left my unit only to lose myself in the jungle, where I wandered until I came upon the village from which I was taken to the Japanese Divisional Headquarters.

I viewed this story from every possible angle, turning it over and over in my mind in an attempt at discovering any flaw. On the whole it seemed to be credible, although there was one weakness which would need careful handling—my small knowledge of Urdu, Hindi, or any other Indian language. I knew only a very little Urdu, not as much as I would have done, if I had lived in India for as long as I was supposed to have done, and I was almost certain to come into contact with Indians at some time or other. For a long time I could see no way out of the difficulty, finally deciding that I would attribute my small knowledge of any Indian language to the long period that I had spent in Europe. It was not too clever, but it was the only explanation that I could concoct.

The car sped on nearer to the city until we passed an imposing group of buildings, which I afterwards learned were the Rangoon University buildings, and came to a roundabout. Soon after this, we passed an extremely fine modern building with a large central tower, Japanese sentries at the gates, and the Japanese Rising Sun flag flying from a pole on the tower. I rightly guessed that it was the Jap Army H.Q. After passing two more roundabouts, the car turned sharp right and drove for a short distance down a tree-lined street, bearing the name 'Cheape Road' on a plate at the corner, and then turned into the gate of a large modern villa, to halt at the front door. A sentry stood at the door, and I noted with surprise that he was an Indian, although he wore the ordinary Japanese uniform, and was armed with a British Lee-Enfield rifle. He drew himself to a position, vaguely reminiscent of the position of attention, as we passed him, and we entered a large hall where we found an Indian wearing an unfamiliar uniform, resembling the khaki bush jacket worn by many officers in India, but with knee breeches and polished Japanese riding boots instead of trousers or shorts. My escort saluted punctiliously and, handing over an envelope which I had not seen before, stood silent. The Indian took the envelope with a very surprised look in my direction and, opening it, unfolded a sheet of paper, which he began to read. As he read the look of surprise on his face deepened and, from the glances that he shot at me, it was easy to guess that all relevant details concerning myself were contained within the letter. I waited, not without misgivings. Then a change came over his face, and he positively beamed, and turning to me said, in English:

"So we have succeeded: this is very good indeed. You have done very well. Please give me the Buddha and I will keep it safe until morning when you will see the Chief. Now you must be very tired and hungry, come with me and I will make you comfortable, as you well deserve."

So saying he dismissed my escort with an airy wave of his hand, and led the way up a flight of stairs. There I was installed in a very pleasant room overlooking a well kept garden; it was well furnished, and I gazed with satisfaction upon a large and comfortable looking bed—a marvellous sight. Clearly I was regarded as a person who had rendered some signal service to the Japanese cause—and that was not a comforting thought. A meal was brought to me to which I did full justice.

The Indian in the unusual uniform appeared, as affable as ever, and after making a few general remarks left me alone, but not before he had requested me not to leave the house and intimated that the sentries had orders to see that I did not. So I was still not above suspicion.

As soon as he had gone I sat down to do some very serious thinking. One thing stood out a mile beyond everything else: I had been the unwitting means whereby the enemy had come into the possession of a very valuable piece of information. That was extremely serious, and somehow or other I must do something about it. For a while I entertained wild notions of creeping downstairs to search for the Buddha so that I might destroy or hide it, but I dismissed that idea as quite impracticable. I should have done that earlier; by this time it would doubtless be under lock and key, and well-guarded if it was as important as was suggested by my flying to Rangoon by special plane. Ought I to reveal my true identity before I did any more damage, or should I wait and see what I could discover? Perhaps I should be honest and admit that it was partly the thought of changing my comfortable position—that wonderful-looking bed—for that of a miserable, badly-treated prisoner-of-war, which finally made me decide to carry on the game a little longer. Anyway that was what I did decide. Had I not done so, this would never have been written. I climbed into the comfortable bed with the growing conviction that I could get away with it, after having got away with so much already—again very unreasonably.

Morning came and, after having breakfasted in my room, I was requested to come downstairs to meet the Chief. As I slowly descended the white-painted staircase, my feet noiseless on the thick stair carpet, once the pride of some English housewife, my former misgivings came over me once again, and I felt like bolting through the open front door and running for it. However, it was too late to draw back, and so I crossed the hall and passed through the doorway into a large room with French windows standing wide open. The room was furnished in the same lavish manner as the rest of the house: a thick, soft carpet covered the floor, and the articles of furniture were well made of dark Burma teak. A large table stood in front of the French windows, and behind it sat four men: two Japanese officers and two Indians, one of the latter being the man who had greeted me when I arrived. He was a man of medium height and somewhat over-weight, with a dark, almost black complexion, clearly a Bengali of the 'Babu' class, with some education if it was only a 'failed B.A.' The other Indian was a Sikh, a big, well-built man, although far from young, for his beard and the unclipped wisps of hair which strayed from under his green turban were quite grey. He wore horn-rimmed spectacles on a somewhat hooked nose, and on his left wrist I could see the steel bangle worn by all orthodox Sikhs. He appeared to be in charge of the proceedings, and I rightly assumed that he must be the Chief.

The two Japanese were majors, small men with round faces wearing thick horn-rimmed spectacles through which they blinked at me in an owlish fashion, and with the inevitable sword strapped to their sides.

On the table in front of the big Sikh stood the little brass Buddha.

The Chief opened the proceedings by motioning me to take a seat. I did so, and then he looked at me fixedly, a proceeding which did nothing to quieten my misgivings, and said in perfect English:

"You have done a notable service to our cause and, for those services, you will be well rewarded. We have been expecting the information that you have brought for some time, and it has arrived just at the right moment. I have received a letter from the commander of the 84th Japanese Infantry Regiment giving most of the details of your arrival at his H.Q. but there are some points which are not very clear, and I would be obliged if you would tell us the story youself."

I had no option, and so I started off on my previously prepared story. Fortunately for me, I now had the whole invention off pat, and I was able to tell a connected story, and answer the questions which were put to me without hesitation. I told the tale of my grievance, and made as much of it as I could. I pointed out that I was half French, that I had spent the greater part of my life in France, and firmly believed that Marshal Petain was a great leader who would restore the French nation to greatness, alongside the German and Japanese people. I was rather vague about the man who had first contacted me in Calcutta, naturally enough since so far as I knew he did not exist, but that part of the story was swallowed without hesitation; so there must in actual fact have been just such a man in the pay of the Japanese in Calcutta at that particular time—scarcely a surprising fact. I was able to describe the man from whom I had obtained the statue at Dimapur fairly accurately. That was fairly easy since he did really exist, and I had seen him.

Suddenly the Chief broke into Hindustani, and I realised that I was then skating over the thin ice. Fortunately I grasped the trend of what he was saying, and replied in French, saying that I was not very familiar with any of the Indian languages having lived for so long in France. One of the Japanese officers then answered me in French, which he spoke quite well, and we held a short conversation.

"That is good," said the Chief. "We had expected that the bearer of the information would be a citizen of one of the nations of the Greater East Asia Co-prosperity Sphere, and we were very surprised to see one, whom we thought at first to be an Englishman; at first I was inclined to suspect that it was a trick. Now it is clear that you are what you claim to be, and in any case you have brought this extremely valuable information to us."

I muttered something about being only too glad to be of service in the liberation of India from the hands of the brutal British oppressors. Then he went on:

"Since you have performed such a dangerous, and difficult piece of work so well, it is only fair that you should know more. This is the headquarters of the Babu Amar Singh Espionage Group, the espionage organisation of the Azad Hind, the Free Indian Government of our noble leader, Subhas Chandra Bose. I am the head of this espionage group, and you have brought information which will enable the Japanese Imperial Forces, assisted by our Indian National Army, to sweep the British from India for ever. Soon our glorious flag will be flying over the Red Fort at Delhi, alongside the Rising Sun of Nippon, and we shall go forward working with our Japanese leaders, to build the Greater East Asia Co-prosperity Sphere."

He paused for breath at the end of this dramatic announcement, and then the whole party, rising to their feet, shouted:

"Banzai! Banzai!"

This performance surprised me; there was a curious air of unreality about the whole pronouncement, the old man speaking as if he was repeating a carefully taught lesson; whilst the concerted shout, although loud enough, lacked sincerity. It was more like the over dramatisation of a third-rate actor than the impassioned outpourings of a sincere patriot.

A brief period of silence ensured, and then the Chief went on to say:

"I have examined the information, and it is very satisfactory, but it appears that your assistance is still needed to bring the whole scheme to fruition, therefore it will be necessary to make you familiar with some of the details of the scheme. But before I say more I must warn you that you must not talk about anything you learn, on pain of death. If any leaks occur you will be held responsible. Still, I think you are to be trusted after what you have done, and you, the bearer of the information, are recommended by our agent as being familiar with the country in question."

"You may rely upon me to do all that I can," I replied, wondering what on earth he was talking about, and fearful lest my ignorance should betray me if he asked me questions concerning 'the country'; whatever, and wherever that was. I need not have worried, the Chief liked to talk, and I was only expected to murmur an affirmative now and then. So I sat silent and waited.

Leaning to one side, he opened a drawer in the table, and produced a round metal box having two long rubber covered leads, with a plug attached to the loose ends. One of the Japanese officers rose to his feet, and picking up the leads plugged them into a power point in the wall. The old Sikh then picked up the little brass Buddha, and stood it on top of the metal box.

I watched, greatly mystified, wondering what it was all about as he picked a large pair of pliers from the drawer, and proceeded to insert a piece of cloth into the jaws.

At a word from the Chief the Jap officer pressed the switch at the side of the power point—and I almost expected the Buddha to start talking after such mysterious preparations—needless to say it did nothing of the kind, in fact nothing happened. Then the Chief, grasping the lower part of the Buddha with his left hand, gripped the head with the cloth-protected pliers, still keeping the image standing on the metal box, and began to unscrew the body from the head.

I saw it all; it was a mystery no longer. The Buddha did open. The information was inside it. The metal box was nothing but a powerful electro-magnet, which, when the current was switched on, pulled down a spring-loaded iron or steel plunger inside the body of the idol which had previously locked the head in position, preventing it from being unscrewed.

He continued to unscrew the head until it came right off, disclosing a hole perhaps half-an-inch in diameter, bored down the centre of the body. To the side of this hole was a smaller hole, with a corresponding one in the head, and as the Jap officer switched off the current I saw a steel plunger rise above the top of the smaller hole in the body. The statuette, being made of brass, was naturally unaffected by the electro-magnet, whilst the steel plunger would be drawn against the pressure of a concealed spring. The joint between the body and head was very finely machined and concealed by the collar round the neck of the Buddha.

It was such an ingenious arrangement that I fear that my mouth dropped open in amazement. The squat form of the Buddha rendered it peculiarly suitable for the adaption, and I have no doubt that a quantity of lead had been incorporated in the base when it was manufactured so that no suspicious lightness would be evident. Furthermore, the possession of such an article could not possibly arouse the slightest suspicion, particularly when the owner was a Burman, and a Buddhist, as the intended owner had been. I could see no reason for the unorthodox arrangement of the arms, but I imagine that it was deliberately designed to be different from a normal Buddha, so that it could be easily recognised by the Jap troops who would be warned to look out for a man carrying such an article.

The Chief picked the Buddha up, turned it upside

down, and tapped the base sharply. A roll of paper secured by a rubber band fell out, which he proceeded to unroll. He unrolled it very carefully, for the paper was very thin and tightly rolled; it must have been nearly three feet in length, and covered with fine writing and neatly drawn diagrams. So very simple really; here was information which could not be sent by wireless, or any such means; whilst the method of using one of Wingate's Chindits as the bearer of the information, was both audacious and effective. I was to learn that there was even more to it than that. It was apparent that the enemy had been aware that a second Wingate expedition was being prepared, although they probably knew few details, a state of affairs which should have been rectified by the arrival of the special messenger. Needless to say I had every intention of saying as little about that as I could.

On the face of it the scheme would seem bound to succeed, and it was only one chance in a million which had led to the Buddha falling into my hands. Who could have foreseen that I should blunder on the conspirators at the very moment when the idol was being handed over? Or that neither of the two men would do anything about the matter, after it had fallen into the wrong hands?

I thought about this very deeply, and finally decided that the Burman must have been too frightened to do or say anything, fearing that the statuette had fallen into the hands of an officer, and relying upon not having been recognised to keep him safe. As for the Indian: he may also have thought that it had fallen into the hands of an officer, and believing that all would soon be discovered, had washed his hands of the whole affair, trusting also to not having been identified. Whatever the explanation, the fact remained that the enemy were not aware that the information had fallen into the wrong hands.

Suddenly the other Indian, hitherto silent, spoke:

"You are familiar with the country in the area of Dimapur?"

"Yes," I said, hoping that was the right answer, and realising that the information that I had brought was connected in some way with that place.

"How do you know that place?"

"I was stationed in that part of Assam for some time," I replied, thinking of that explanation on the spur of the moment.

"That is good," he said, subsiding back into his chair.

The big Sikh then leaned forward, and lowering his voice to almost a whisper, said:

"Now you will pay great attention. The information that you have brought to us will enable a force of the I.N.A., assisted by the Japanese Imperial Forces, to seize a vitally important objective in that area when the time comes. You have been recommended to us as a guide, because you are familiar with the area, and also because you have proved yourself to be reliable. Now look at this diagram."

As he said this he drew a sheet of paper over most of the scroll spread out on the table so that I should not see what else was written on it, and directed my attention to a little map, very carefully drawn at one end of the paper. It showed a stretch of the Assam Railway, Dimapur Station, and a part of the Assam Trunk Road.

"The scheme is this," he went on. "At the right moment a Task Force of the Japanese Imperial Army and the I.N.A. will arrive at this point here, just north of Ukhrul, and it will be your task to guide that Force along a track which we understand you know, over the hills to the railway east of Dimapur. This Force will then set up a rail block to stop all traffic, and will hold that block until the main body of the Japanese Army is able to reach the railway. Meanwhile you will guide the I.N.A. element to the garage of Suleiman Ismail and Sons on the road, where a number of buses and other vehicles are kept ready for use. You will then lead these buses along the road, avoiding Dimapur itself, to a spot west of the town, and then guide them back to the railway where another block will be established. By this means we shall be able to put the railway out of action, and prevent the arrival of all stores and reinforcements at Dimapur, at a time when they will be most needed; and also close the line of supply to the Americans and Chinese in the north of Assam, and prevent any further supplies from being taken to the American airfields, from which they are now being flown to China."

"As a reward for the services that you have already rendered to the liberation of India, I am directed to inform you that you have been appointed to the honorary rank of Captain in the Indian National Army. Arrangements will be made to supply you with suitable uniform, and, until such time as your services are required, you will remain here. I will arrange a suitable escort so that you may leave the house from time to time. You will, however, remember the warning to keep silent. Other details will be arranged later. Is that clear?"

It was only too clear, as was also the gravity of the situation which I had unwittingly precipitated. I had been the means of bringing this information to the Japanese, and it weighed heavily upon my mind and conscience, even though I had been ignorant of the true nature of what I was carrying.

I managed to mutter that it was all clear, hoping that the dismay that I felt would not show in my expression. I was in this business right up to the neck now. I had done the damage, and my only thought was to rectify, somehow or other, the damage that I had already succeeded in doing. There was only one bright spot, one solitary gleam of hope. I was above suspicion, or almost so, but above everything else, they were relying on me to act as a guide—talk of the blind leading the blind! If I went about things in the right way I might yet manage to put a spoke in their wheel, although how it could be done was quite another matter.

My interview was at an end, and I left the room, and made my way up the stairs to my room to ponder what I had learned—and I had some thinking to do. I spent the whole of the remainder of the day thinking, and thinking, and in the end came to the conclusion that I must bide my time. I could do nothing where I was.

OBSERVER IN RANGOON

THE Indian officer who had first greeted me at Babu Singh's was assigned to me as escort, and since he was disposed to be friendly, I cultivated his acquaintance as much as I possibly could. It appeared that he had been born in Rangoon, and never been to India in his life. Before the war he was employed on the clerical staff of the Rangoon Municipality, and had joined the I.N.A. soon after the Japanese arrived in Rangoon. He was full of the sense of his own importance, and held forth at great length on the subject of the I.N.A., past, present, and future, with great emphasis on his own connection therewith. So far as I could gather, he had had no previous military experience, and had been no nearer to any danger than Rangoon. Despite this slight handicap he was full of contempt for the degenerate British, and their mercenary Indian levies, who were, according to him, already coming over to the I.N.A. in crowds, in a manner which left the Italians cold! His sense of his own importance as an officer of the I.N.A. and member of Babu Singh's Espionage Group, often made him indiscreet in his efforts to impress me; a failing which I encouraged by every means within my power.

His name was Bannerjee, Captain Bannerjee, with great emphasis upon the word 'Captain', it being a title of which he was inordinately proud. He took me around with him on every possible occasion in his car, with the express object of impressing me, taking the very greatest delight in driving up to one of the several I.N.A. Camps to collect salutes; which he did with an air of pompous condescension.

As a consequence, although my stay in Rangoon was a short one—I was there for just one week, in that short time I managed to see and learn quite a lot. I made the maximum use of my limited freedom, and my only thought was to discover all that I could, making copious mental notes, not daring to commit my discoveries to writing. I was able to discover the contents of some of the larger warehouses on the docks, and these I noted in the hope that the R.A.F. would be able to use that information. Most important of all I managed to discover the actual locations of the offices and residences, of Subhas Chandra Bose, Dr. Ba Maw, the puppet Burmese Premier, General Aung San, head of the Burmese Peoples' Army, the Jap C. in C. and the Kempai H.Q.—Jap Gestapo; in addition I noted the position of an ammunition factory, and large ammunition dump north of the city.

Besides this, I saw many little incidents, of no particular importance, but which threw into strong relief the methods employed by the Japanese in running Burma. I was given a vast wad of paper money of all denominations of rupees, and informed that I could have more when I needed it. These notes, printed on very poor quality paper, had no water mark and no serial number, and forgery would be a very simple matter; although I doubt if it would have paid any forger to make them, considering the vast numbers in which they were turned out by the Japanese themselves. Every Jap unit of any size had its own printing press, and by this means as much money as was required could be manufactured; a delightfully simple system which had already produced tremendous inflation. This in itself was a curious sidelight upon the Japanese mentality. The people most affected by this inflation were the better-class educated Burmese, and these were the very people to whom the

Japanese promises of independence for Burma should have appealed and towards whom most of the propaganda was directed. Such a policy of seemingly deliberate inflation could only result in the alienation of any sympathy which these people might have felt towards the Japanese. The poorer people were not so much affected; the Japanese paid all their employees of the coolie class fantastically high wages, which produced an artificial improvement in their standard of living that could not possibly last in a country where consumer goods of every kind were becoming shorter with each passing day. It appeared to me that the Japanese had no intention of staying in Burma for very long; everything was being run on a short term basis, exactly as though they intended to make hay whilst the sun shone and then leave someone else to sort out the mess.

Nothing was brought into the country, apart from what was necessary to maintain the Army, but a great deal of loot was being sent out. The European shops and houses were stripped of all furnishings and fittings for shipment back to Japan. I even saw a party of Japanese removing the marble steps from the front of the famed Strand Hotel; although it is difficult to imagine what they intended to do with them.

So far as I could see, the Japanese had no effective equivalent to our R.A.S.C. and the system of feeding their troops was to send a purchasing party to the market every morning; and they bought all they required with worthless paper money. The result, of course, was that the Japanese got the best of everything. By no stretch of imagination could this be calculated to endear the Japs to the Burmese.

Of course the active Burmese collaborators were well enough off. They also had money to buy whatever they needed, but they were a very small minority. Almost everyone else suffered in some way as a result of the occupation. Many of the better-class civilians had been turned out of their requisitioned houses without adequate compensation, and the necessities of life, apart from food, were becoming ever shorter.

On the whole the Indian community did fairly well, for at that time the Japs were deliberately wooing the Indians in an effort to obtain recruits for the I.N.A. This also did not please the Burmans, as the Indians, generally speaking, are not popular in Burma, most of them being low-type Indians from the south of India who had been imported to form a source of cheap labour.

The Chinese did not do so well; after all they were nationals of one of Japan's enemies.

Signs of neglect were evident in the city. The roads were beginning to break up, and no attempt whatever was made to repair them. The Municipal Services had broken down completely, and piles of refuse and filth of every description littered the streets, together with the debris from the bombed buildings which lay where it had been blown. Even the bomb craters in the streets were only filled in if they happened to interfere with the activities of the Jap Army.

A good deal of quite well produced propaganda literature was available, and I read many of the magazines. Most of them were printed in Japanese, Chinese, French, English and Burmese, so that they could be distributed in any of the Japanese-occupied countries. One was similar to the American magazine *Life,* and from its pages I gleaned many interesting pieces of information. There was one very good photograph of the sinking of the British aircraft-carrier *Hermes* in the Indian Ocean which attracted my attention. Much of the propaganda, however, was quite absurd. Particularly did I note that no Japanese aircraft were ever reported as lost; they either 'all returned to their bases safely' or were 'deliberately crashed upon the enemy', whilst large numbers of British and American planes were always shot down! The cartoons were childish: I remember one which showed an angular British Tommy with a face resembling Sir Winston Churchill's—a contradiction in itself—bent double in excruciating agony whilst an enormous Jap soldier—another contradiction—bored a hole through his back with a large brace and bit.

It must not be supposed that I walked around Rangoon in my tattered old uniform. I was provided with two uniforms, one the ordinary uniform of a Japanese officer, and the other that of an officer in the I.N.A., the uniform that I have already described as being worn by Bannerjee. I was not given a sword, but in all other particulars my dress was that of an officer of the enemy forces. It was the last thing that I expected when I had learned that I had 'volunteered' for L.R.P. work, but for all that it was quite true, and I really was walking around the heart of the Jap organisation in Burma, dressed as an enemy officer.

One day we walked into Rangoon from Babu Singh's H.Q. where I had still continued to live, going by way of the Prome Road, which meant that I had to pass the back of Rangoon Jail. Now I was aware that the jail was used as a P.O.W. Camp, but I had seen none of the prisoners, and I am afraid had thought very little about them. I was walking along the road in a pre-occupied manner, busy with my thoughts, when a very English voice broke upon my reverie.

"You—— ——! You—— —— of a slant eyed—— you!"

I stopped dead, and, to my horror, I saw about half a dozen British prisoners-of-war working in the ditch at the side of the road, guarded by a single Japanese sentry. This savage voice was emanating from one of the men in the ditch as he worked with his head bent. I suppose that he was referring to the sentry, although he may well have been referring to the whole Japanese race in general. In any case the sentry did not appear to be aware of the meaning of the uncomplimentary remarks. I stood stock still, and gazed at my unfortunate fellow countrymen, forced to work under the most degrading conditions possible. They were almost naked, two of them wearing the tattered remnants of a pair of shorts filthy beyond description, whilst the others wore only a G-string. The G-string consists simply of a piece of string tied round the waist, with a narrow piece of cloth, looped into the string at back and front, passed between the legs. They were bare-footed, and plastered with oozy, smelly mud from the ditch up to their thighs, and their bodies were dirty, with numbers of unpleasant looking sores on most of them. None of them had shaved or had a haircut for months, perhaps for as much as a year, and the matted hair about face and head hung together in greasy tangled skeins. All were pitifully thin, without being exactly emaciated, showing that they received just sufficient food to keep them alive and able to work.

I gazed long enough for this to register upon my mind, and then with some muttered excuse to Bannerjee I turned tail and almost bolted. I could not face them. I hurried back to Babu Singh's in such a dreadful state of mind and conscience that I nearly blurted out the whole story to the mystified Bannerjee who fortunately did not appear to guess the reason for my discomfiture—but not quite—I was sobered by the realisation that such precipitate action could have only one ending: I knew too much. I would never be put into an ordinary prison camp to be ill-used as an ordinary P.O.W. My fate would be the sharp edge of a sword—across my neck. Having wormed my way so far into the confidence of the enemy, I could only be one of two things: I was genuine, or I was a particularly audacious spy. It was much too late for anyone to believe that I had been the victim of a most extraordinary chain of coincidence. So I had to stifle the pangs of conscience as well as I could and with an almost superman effort I managed to regain my equanimity.

After I had recovered from this incident, and despite the strain under which I was living and the uncertainty of the future, I took a great delight in wandering with Bannerjee through the streets of Rangoon, where there was always much of interest to be seen. The streets were thronged with people going about their business, and living their everyday lives. There were Burmese, Indians and Chinese, as well as a few Japanese civilians, providing a striking contrast in dress and custom. The three races were represented in roughly equal proportions, and of them the Burmese women were the most colourful, with their slight figures clad in brightly-coloured, ankle length *lungyis,* tightly fitting white bodices, and a little muslin jacket. Their glossy black hair, many coloured parasols, and, quite frequently, enormous white cheroots gripped between their lips completed a gay picture. The better class women had carefully powdered faces, imitated, not too successfully, by their poorer sisters whose faces always appeared to me to have been rather carelessly whitewashed. Unlike the peacock, the peculiarly Burmese symbol, the Burmese men were very much less colourful than their women folk, being usually darker-skinned, although they also wore the same coloured skirt-like *lungyi* with an ordinary shirt, and brown varnished topees made of split bamboo, The Indians provided the usual contrast of poverty and affluence: the men clad in their dhoties, some white and gleaming, others mere fragments of filthy cloth, and the women, with jewelled ears, fingers, and noses, wearing silken saris, or grimy, bedraggled, and clad in some ragged apology for a garment. The other third of the community, the Chinese, presented a completely different picture, their women, some of them extremely attractive, were clad in suits of pyjama-like garments, some gaily-coloured, others a dark, sober blue; and the men wore skirt-like garments and ordinary shirts.

Here, food was being sold at the edge of the pavement, masses of sticky sweetmeats covered with horrible black flies, the vendors squatting alongside quite unconcerned, or perhaps manufacturing more of their particular commodity over a charcoal brazier. There, at a street corner, surrounded by the thronging passers-by, a group of women and children were washing themselves at a gushing hydrant. Rickshaws, the most ramshackle that I have ever seen, wended their way through the crowds, drawn by broken-down Indians wearing flat conical tin hats. Trishaws, odd combinations of a bicycle and an improvised sidecar, were pedalled past at a snail's pace by languid Burmese youths. A few odd cars and buses crammed with people snorted past, emitting the most nauseating stench of burning paraffin oil. I have never ceased to wonder at these vehicles, mostly of American origin and therefore not designed to last, old to the point of being archaic, carrying an astonishing variety of home-made bodies; some of them even had thatched roofs, yet managing to lurch along on threadbare tyres, belching forth clouds of blue smoke. One vehicle in particular attracted my attention; it was a very old Austin car, converted into a small bus by adding a disproportionately large body which hung over the back wheels by about eight feet, and was surmounted by a corrugated iron roof. A small boy sat on the bonnet working the throttle by hand according to directions given by the driver, and received with his left hand a tin of water from a man seated by the side of the driver; this he proceeded to pour into the radiator, from the cap of which, despite the constant replenishment of cold water, clouds of steam issued. I make a bow to the mechanics who managed to keep those vehicles running. Not that they always succeeded, for I saw one or two very badly broken down, still full of a completely unconcerned body of passengers, who apparently imagined that, having paid their fare, they were entitled to sit where they were until repairs were affected. I even saw an engine being completely stripped by the roadside, with the cylinder head removed and the pistons out!

A few trams were running, but only a few, because of the shortage of electric power. I learned that the Japanese were actually feeding the furnaces at the Power Station with a mixture of rice husks and sawdust, having run out of coal.

Over this scene of noise and bustle towered the Sule Pagoda, smaller than the Shwe Dagon, but still imposing with its gilded surface, and the many turretted shrines surrounding it. The painted Buddhas in the shrines looked on with their bland, inscrutable faces, and the saffron-robed, shaven-headed Buddhist Priests made their endless prostrations around the base of the Pagoda, or went about the streets receiving gifts of food from the vendors.

During this time I often wondered what was happening to my comrades in the column, for about that time the Japanese propaganda radio began to admit that British troops were active in North Burma—although of course they were being dealt with. I also wondered sentimentally about Mary, and how she was getting on with her lonely life amongst the uneducated villagers.

Bannerjee talked a good deal about the coming big offensive which was to sweep the British out of India for ever, hinting broadly that he was in the know. I pumped him as cautiously as I could, not wishing to appear to be too interested, and finally discovered that the special Task Force, composed of both Japanese and I.N.A. troops, was waiting to move up as soon as the offensive was well under way. This was the Task Force which I was expected to guide from Ukhrul to Dimapur. I also managed to find out that this Force occupied some barracks just off the Kokine Road, north of the city. This was one of the camps that I visited with Bannerjee, and so I got a preview of the men with whom I should soon be travelling to the north of Burma. I was not impressed by what I saw; generally speaking their quality was low—I refer to the I.N.A. element of course—and they were a weird mixture of Sikhs, Garhwalis, Punjabis, and the little Indians native to the Rangoon area. I knew very little about Indian troops at that time, but I was sure that such a diverse mixture of types and races would not hold together very well in a tight corner. I suspected that this crowd of odds and ends was given such a task for purely political reasons, and in any case the real burden would fall upon the Japanese part of the Force.

I saw little of their officers then; that was to come later, but what I did see told me that the majority of them were of the same calibre as my 'friend' Bannerjee. The C.O. of the I.N.A. troops was, however, a very different proposition. Like the Chief, he was a Sikh; a former regular officer of the Indian Army with ample military training, and he looked a capable individual. He had, I learned, been taken prisoner in Malaya, and had obtained his freedom by agreeing to join the I.N.A., thinking, I suppose, that the gamble was worth-while seeing that he would attain a high position in the I.N.A. if the Japs did succeed in conquering India. I caught a glimpse of him on one of my visits to the Kokine Road Camp with

Bannerjee; a tall, well built man with a fine black beard, trimmed to a neat point in the manner adopted by some of the modern Sikhs. He almost ignored Bannerjee's ostentatious salute as he stalked past us, and I felt that he had such contempt for officers like Bannerjee that he could not bring himself to notice their existence.

JAPANESE RAIDING PARTY

ONE day the Japanese publicity and propaganda machinery was turned on at its highest pressure with the announcement that the great attack had begun. The victorious Japanese Army, or so it was reported, was driving all before it in the wildest confusion. The 17th Indian Division had been routed, and driven in disorder from Tiddim with the loss of all its equipment. The Indian border had been reached and Imphal threatened. The British Air Force had been shot from the skies. It was the beginning of the end of the domination of the White races, and soon the Azad Hind would be established in New Delhi, under the protection of the Japanese Imperial Forces to complete the Greater East Asia Co-prosperity Sphere.

Special editions of the Japanese controlled newspapers with huge headlines appeared, together with numerous pamphlets and handbills, special broadcast programmes presented, and a grand demonstration staged in Rangoon. Lecturers harangued the crowds at every street corner, and the I.N.A. collected many recruits, attracted by the dazzling prospect of returning to India as great men and conquerors.

Bannerjee insisted on taking me to witness the demonstration, even though I did my best to get out of going, fearful still of appearing in any public place. Detachments of the Japanese Army, the B.P.A. and the I.N.A., were to assemble at various points in the city, march to the golf course in front of the Shwe Dagon Pagoda, there to be treated to a series of speeches by Dr. Ba Maw and Subhas Chandra Bose.

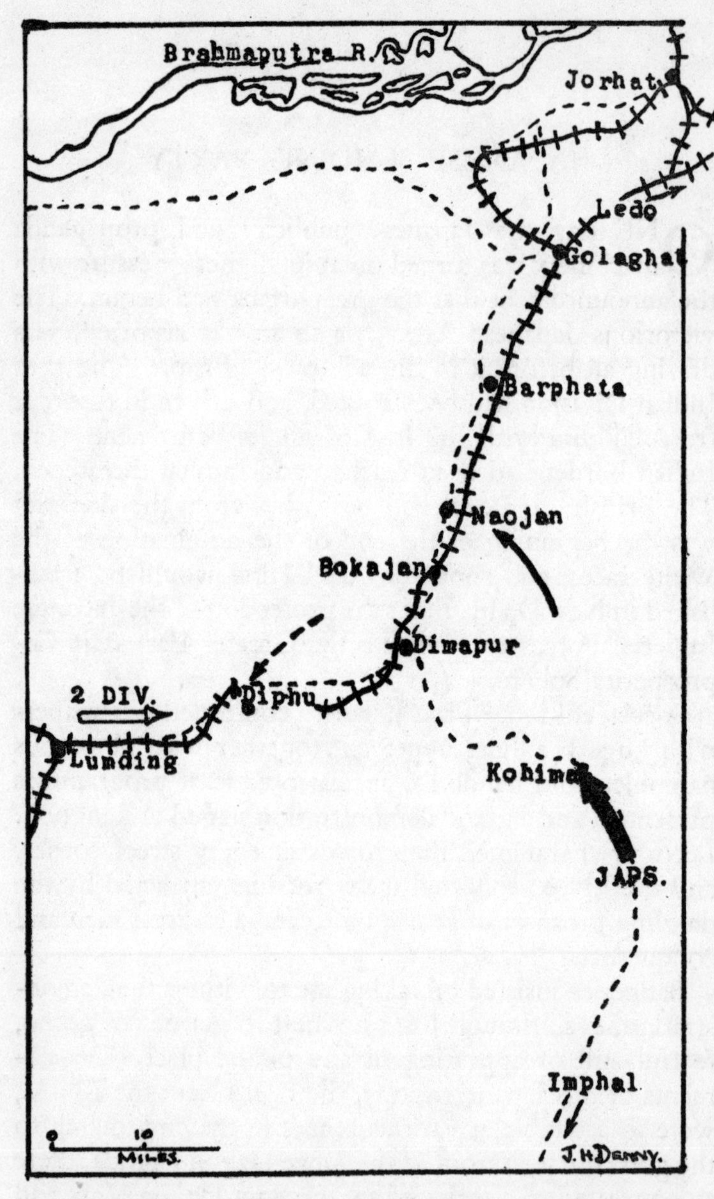

DIAGRAMMATIC MAP OF THE ASSAM RAILWAY, THE OBJECTIVE OF THE JAP AND I.N.A. ATTACK THAT THE AUTHOR HELPED TO FOIL.

We drove along the Prome Road in Bannerjee's car, specially polished for the occasion, and complete with a small Indian Nationalist flag, horizontally striped in orange, white, and green, bearing the device of a spinning wheel, and arrived well before the demonstration was due to start. A stage had been erected, and large crowds had gathered to witness this spectacle of Japanese military might. The spectators had been marshalled into the shape of a huge three-sided hollow square, thus enabling the troops to parade in the centre. It was late afternoon and the declining sun shone upon the colourful scene, and the mass of the Shwe Dagon Pagoda was in the background, so that the whole gilded surface of the Pagoda was a blaze of golden light. The feathery palm trees growing round the base of the Pagoda swayed gently in the light breeze, and the pinnacled spires of the Pagoda shrines clustering round about were plainly visible in the strong light, even down to the details of their fantastic carvings. A continuous murmur arose from the crowd, impatient for the show to begin, the pinks, greens, and yellows of their garments blending into a single blaze of vivid colour.

At last there was a blast of noisy Eastern music from half a dozen loud speakers, and the crowd surged forward a little at this signal that the show was beginning. A group of Burmese and Indian civilians emerged from behind a large screen and arranged themselves on the platform, the Burmese in a group on one side, the Indians in a similar group on the other side, with a space left in the middle. A pause followed whilst these groups were arranged, and another, and louder blast of music followed, announcing the entrance of another group consisting of a few Japanese civilians clad in Western clothes, and a number of high-ranking Japanese officers, belted and sworded, resplendent with a galaxy of medal ribbons, and wearing white shirts with the collars outside their tunics; an incongruous feature to my way of thinking.

Bannerjee was chattering away like an excited magpie at my side. It was a great day for him and he was at the top of his form.

"Think of it," he burst out, unable to contain his elation, "Soon I shall be a Colonel and a very important man; so much better than when I was just a little clerk working for the British."

Then he went on to point out the various dignitaries on the platform.

"There is the Commander-in-Chief," said he pointing to a portly bespectacled Japanese officer. "Next to him in the dark grey suit and butterfly wing collar, wearing horn-rimmed glasses is Mr. Reno Sawada, the Japanese Ambassador to the Burma Independence Committee."

"Who are the Indians and Burmese?" I asked.

"That is the Burmese Independence Preparatory Committee, and the man in the centre, wearing the white jacket and the striped, coloured *lungyi*, with the pink head cloth is Dr. Ba Maw. The Indians are the Provisional Azad Hind, and the man in the centre is our great Babu Subhas Chandra Bose himself."

I looked at the last named with interest, having heard a good deal about the ex-Congress leader heading the so-called Indian Government. I saw the figure of a middle-aged dark-complexioned Indian with a marked paunch, wearing the uniform of an officer of the I.N.A.; light khaki bush jacket and knee breeches with polished Japanese knee boots, complete with shining spurs—a totally unnecessary addition, I thought, since he looked too fat to ride a horse. Set squarely on his head, and slightly too large for him, was a khaki forage cap. A pair of thick horn-rimmed spectacles perched on his nose, with the appearance of having slipped down, completed the picture. He reminded me of nothing so much as an ordinary Indian Bazaar Babu, professional letter writer, or money-lender; and was altogether a most unimpressive figure for the leader of a National uprising.

Whilst all this had been happening, the troops, Japanese for the most part, but with some I.N.A. men and a few Burmese, had begun to arrive together with a contingent of uniformed Indian women wearing khaki shirts and shorts. I asked Bannerjee who they were, and he said that they were women of the Rani of Jhansi Regiment, women auxiliaries of the I.N.A. and, I suspected, camp followers. The Japanese troops were dressed in the usual fashion, but the Indians wore British Army khaki shirts and shorts and carried Lee-Enfield rifles, doubtless part of stocks captured from us in 1942. The only articles of Japanese origin they wore were boots of canvas and rubber.

The drill was slovenly by our standards, and the Indians in particular shambled along in and out of step. After a little confusion they were drawn up in line facing the platform, and at a word from their officers the Japanese troops waved their rifles in the air, and shouted: "Banzai! Banzai!" whilst the I.N.A. troops chanted the slogan "Jai Hind" (Hail India). As if by magic a thousand little flags appeared above the heads of the spectators, and were waved by a thousand hands as the spectators joined in the shouts. These flags must have been issued to the crowd specially for the purpose, for they were all the same, a red circle on a white ground.

Then the speech-making began, of which I understood not a single word. First of all Chandra Bose spoke, then Ba Maw, and last of all the Japanese Ambassador. It went on and on, and at intervals the crowd raised a shout and waved their flags, in such a mechanical fashion that I am convinced that they were being prompted from the rear.

I thought it would never finish, as I stood there shifting from one leg to the other, whilst Bannerjee, who was in an ecstacy of delight, would now and then nudge me and grin expansively, thinking, I feel sure, that he would soon be standing on a similar platform somewhere in India, making an impressive speech to a wildly-cheering flag-waving crowd.

At long, long last it came to an end, and the troops marched off. Bannerjee and I climbed into the car and drove back to Babu Singh's H.Q. On the way back he said:

"I think that the Chief will have something to say to you very soon."

I tried to get him to reveal more, but for once he was silent, and I could get nothing out of him. An uneasy feeling crossed my mind, But I could only wait in growing trepidation, and see.

Sure enough, soon after we arrived back I was informed that the Chief wanted to see me, and I presented myself in fear and trembling to the same room where I had had my previous interview. I was reassured as soon as I entered the room by the Chief smiling genially and asking me to be seated. He was not alone, a Japanese officer I had never seen before was with him, and he was introduced to me as Major Tagachaki, the C.O. of the mixed Task Force which was shortly to make the attack on the Assam Railway. The old Sikh did all the talking.

"Things are going so well in the north that it is necessary to despatch the Force at once. You will accompany them as a guide and will have no other duties. Our troops are striking for Imphal, whilst others are advancing upon Ukhrul; that is all that I can tell you, but the details will be arranged by the commander of the

Japanese forward troops and Major Tagachaki, and you will be told more later."

He handed me a map of the Imphal and Dimapur areas, and went on:

"This map has been specially prepared for your use, and gives as much detail as is possible to obtain, which unfortunately is not very much since the British have never made a proper survey of that wild country. That is why you, with your detailed knowledge of that part of Assam, have been selected to act as guide. Great things depend upon you, and you will be well rewarded if you successfully carry out this mission. Tomorrow you will leave for the north with the Force, and I want you to go along with Major Tagachaki now."

I received this information in silence, but my brain was busy. I didn't like the sound of this Japanese attack which seemed to be going so well, and I wondered why I had heard so little of my own comrades. I know now, of course, that they were very far from idle, but the Jap propaganda machine was not advertising such unpleasant facts. The trust the enemy placed in me was rather bewildering, and my efforts at guiding the Task Force should be interesting when the time came.

The Chief rose to his feet as a sign that the interview was at an end, and shook hands with me effusively. I went away to pack my few belongings, and in a few minutes I was seated by the side of Major Tagachaki being driven to the I.N.A. Barracks in the Kokine Road.

I spent that night under very uncomfortable conditions; the whole camp being upside down as frantic efforts were made to be ready to move on the following morning. I slept in a *basha* by myself. In that I was fortunate since everyone else was up all night packing and sorting things out; but I was just the guide.

Morning came; and I was able to see the whole body of

the Force as it paraded preparatory to moving to the station. As far as I could see it numbered about five hundred men; about one hundred and fifty were Indian, and the remainder Japanese. Every man, Indian as well as Japanese, wore ordinary Japanese uniform, and was armed with the ordinary Japanese rifle. I imagine that the difficulties in the way of supplying .303 ammunition precluded the use of captured British rifles in forward areas.

We were all taken by truck to the Insein Railway Station, where we were to entrain. Few vehicles were provided, and the troops were crammed into the trucks like so many animals, although I, being an officer, travelled quite comfortably in the front of one of the vehicles.

As we approached the Insein Station, the first thing I saw was a whole siding full of rusty derelict engines, each as full of bullet holes as a colander. The boilers of some of them had burst and were mere masses of twisted steel, and such an eloquent testimony to the effectiveness of the R.A.F.'s train-busting operations filled me with delight not unmixed with dismay. I had no particular desire to be strafed by the long range Beaufighters.

The train in which we were to travel was drawn up in the station, itself much bombed and battered, although at first I did not recognise it for what it was. It consisted almost entirely of steel goods wagons, with two ordinary passenger coaches at the rear, reserved for the officers. I noticed that these coaches had been placed as far away from the engine as possible, a wise precaution so far as the officers were concerned, since it was always the engine which the pilots tried to destroy. Furthermore the I.N.A. troops were to travel in the wagons next to the engine—a significant fact! Twenty-five men were packed into each wagon, and twenty-five men in an all-steel railway wagon without windows, and the sides too hot to touch from the blazing tropical sun overhead, must have been rather unpleasant for the men in question.

The officers were quite comfortable, and I found myself sharing a compartment with three I.N.A. officers. The Japanese officers would have little to do with me—a white, or near-white man; I was beneath their contempt; and very little to do with the Indians either, who were only just worthy of their notice. Despite the propaganda line of the Greater East Asia Co-prosperity Sphere, the individual Jap officers and men made no secret of their true feelings towards the Indians. The Japanese were the conquerors, and the Indians destined to be their subjects. The only Indian who was treated with respect was the Sikh Commander of the I.N.A. element, but even he, although a Lieut-Colonel, took orders from Major Tagachaki who was only a Major after all.

The three Indians who travelled with me all knew some English, which, strangely enough, they insisted upon speaking. The Japanese had made determined attempts to substitute Japanese for Western cultural influences in their base areas; great emphasis being laid upon the teaching of Nippon salutations, Nippon manners and customs, the inculcation of Nippon-Seishin (the Japanese Spirit), the supersession of the Western handshake by the Japanese bow, and above all by the official prohibition of English and the fostering of Nippon-Go (the Japanese language) as the *lingua franca* of the Greater East Asia Co-prosperity Sphere. But despite these efforts English was still widely spoken, purely practical considerations ensuring that this must be so. They all had been born outside of India, two of them in Singapore, and the other in Rangoon, and were like Bannerjee in many respects, partially-educated men of the Babu Class, who had joined the I.N.A. from similar ignoble motives. Their names were Ghosh, Parkash, and Das Gupta; short, dark, portly men, and Ghosh wore spectacles through which he blinked owlishly at his surroundings, as if unable to focus the objects he saw.

After a lengthy wait the train finally started, passing first of all through the bomb-shattered Rangoon Railway Station before turning north. Once again I was travelling to a forward area as a member of a raiding party—but with what a difference! I think that I can lay claim to be the only man in the British Army in the 1939-45 War who has been a member of a raiding party of the enemy forces as well as his own.

So it was that I sat thinking as the metre-gauge train rattled forward into the unknown, and my thoughts went back to the beginning of the whole business, to the Officers' Mess, Gibraltar Barracks, Aldershot, and to that strangely naïve young man who had led that Church Parade the wrong way round. It all seemed so incomprehensible. It just did not seem possible that I was the same person; centuries of time seemed to have passed, and yet in reality it was only a few months. I found it almost incredible, even though I knew that it had really happened. The Buddha was no figment of my imagination, and I did not have to pinch myself to discover that it was no dream, that I, John Denny, was sitting in a railway train in enemy-occupied territory, wearing enemy uniform, and consorting with enemies of the Crown. It was only too real; and I knew that I needed fortune, as good as any that had already come my way, to see me through what lay ahead.

* * *

We travelled in that train as far as the Ava Bridge, south of Mandalay, the only bridge across the Irrawaddy, and there we had to detrain, for the Japanese had been unable to repair the huge broken span, destroyed by the retreating British Forces in 1942. Because of that, the crossing had to be made by ferry, and I got some idea of the difficulties facing the Japanese commanders in getting supplies to their troops. Every single article had to be laboriously unloaded from the train, carried on to the Country boat ferry, rowed across the river, unloaded again, and carried to the train on the opposite bank.

We made the crossing and found a train waiting on the other bank. It was quite different to the other, consisting of the same type of goods wagon with two passenger coaches, but drawn by three little Diesel-engined locomotives spaced at intervals along the train. It appeared, then, that all the steam loco's on that side of the river had been shot up, and the Nips forced to use these little Diesel substitutes. So far we had been lucky, and no Allied aircraft had been seen.

Soon after we had entrained again, I was thinking how fortunate we had been when I heard the loud wailing of a siren, followed almost immediately by the 'put-put-put' of a light A.A. gun and the roar of aircraft engines. In the twinkling of an eye there was pandemonium as the whole party detrained at ten times the speed with which it had entrained. I was knocked into a corner of the compartment by Messrs. Ghosh, Parkash and Das Gupta as they dived for the door, and, as I scrambled to my feet again, I had a momentary glimpse of the seats of three pairs of trousers as the owners thereof dived for the ditch. Realising that the train was not a healthy place. I also detrained at top speed, but not, I trust, in such an undignified manner as my fellow-travellers. I jumped out of the train and saw that everyone was doing likewise. Within a few moments I had gained the shelter of the ditch in which my travelling companions were already firmly ensconced, devoutly thankful for the friendly shelter it offered. After the first excitement had passed, realising that we were in no immediate danger as the attack was being delivered upon the opposite side of the river, I wriggled myself into a position from which I could see what was happening.

Whilst we had been crossing the river another train drawn by steam locomotion had arrived on the other bank, and that undoubtedly saved us. The pilot, seeing two trains drawn up together would naturally not fail to miss such a favourable target; furthermore it is likely that he thought that our train was without means of locomotion for the Diesel locos were rather like an ordinary wagon in external appearance.

I could see only one plane, a Beaufighter and, even as I watched, it swooped down over one of the trains and flew along the entire length with its guns chattering madly. There was a violent 'swoosh' from the engine, and an enormous cloud of steam suddenly billowed forth, enveloping both engine and tender in a thick white blanket. With a roar the plane swept overhead after completing the attack, so low that I could see the pilot's features as it banked, and I ducked, fearfully expecting to hear the guns breaking into their deadly 'rat-tat-tat'. But it ignored us completely and, turning, dived for the other bank again. This time the other train was the target, and the performance was repeated with even more spectacular results: there was a muffled explosion, and I distinctly saw the boiler of the engine lifted clear of the wheels and tossed to one side before the enveloping steam obscured my vision. I thought that our turn was coming next; but, not so, and after circling round, completely ignoring the A.A. guns, the Beaufighter proceeded to shoot up the ferry boats.

It was ludicrous to watch the crews diving overboard,

and to see the masts come toppling down, and the craft turning turtle and sinking, yet so difficult to realise that over there men were dying in a welter of blood.

With a final roar the plane swept over our heads, and then it was gone as quickly as it it had come. For several minutes no-one dared to move, but, when it was evident that the plane had gone for good, the ditch disgorged its contents, and the air was filled with the chattering of the excited soldiery. Within a short time the Japanese officers restored order by dint of much face slapping, and herded the troops back into the train. It was imperative that the train should move as quickly as possible in case another Beaufighter appeared, but some difficulty was experienced with some of the I.N.A. troops, almost without exception the little Indians recruited in Rangoon. It was not what they expected when they enlisted, dazzled by the seemingly invincible might of the Japanese Army, fed with specious promises of land and wealth in India, and intoxicated by the heady propaganda of 'Jai Hind'. The other Indians, ex-Indian Army men, were stolid enough, and they helped the Japanese to force the crying hysterical men into the wagons again.

I watched this scene with the greatest of interest, reflecting that it offered distinct possibilities for the future, and wondering how I could use this lack of amity between the oddly-assorted allies. It was unfortunate that the better type Indians were so outnumbered, yet if I was careful . . . .?

When I regained the compartment, I saw that my brother I.N.A. officers were also rattled, and I rejoiced inwardly at the sight. Their heads too had been so stuffed with Japanese propaganda that it had never even occurred to them that their lives might be endangered. Had not the R.A.F. been swept from the skies?—— Then how was it that such a daring attack had been carried out with impunity?—— Were the British not fleeing in disorder?—— Or were they?

Ghosh, aptly enough, looked as near like a ghost, as his dark complexion and ample figure would allow, as he sat mopping his grey features with a large handkerchief; and the other two, their nerves on edge, were constantly popping their heads out of the window to see if another plane was coming. I took a malicious delight in playing on their fears as much as I could by simulating a state of abject terror. It had a wonderful effect, and in a short time Ghosh was positively gibbering; then, when I pretended to see a plane circling above the trees in the distance, he was out of the door and into the ditch again before anyone could stop him. I had the greatest difficulty in controlling myself after this amazing exhibition of warlike spirit, particularly when he emerged from the ditch with his hands full of sharp thorns, and his spectacles caked with mud.

Soon after this little incident the train got under way and was scudding along as fast as the Diesel engines would pull it.

After a time my companions controlled their fears, realising that their skins were still whole, and became something like normal again; but they were subdued men, mere shadows of their former ebullient selves. The Beaufighter attack had set them thinking and visualising all sorts of unpleasant possibilities. During the whole of the four hundred mile journey from Rangoon to the Ava Bridge near Mandalay, I had had to endure their fatuous never-ending remarks. They had only one topic of conversation, which boiled down to singing the praises of the matchless I.N.A., and the illustrious Subhas Chandra Bose. It had started soon after we left Insein Railway Station, and had gone on as the train rattled north through the vast expanse of paddy fields, brown with the stubble from the rice harvest. Pegu, Pyu, and Toungoo, (the latter place made me think of Mary again) and with Toungoo the end of the double track railway, had come and gone, and still the same flow of talk went on.

"Such a dignified man," Ghosh would say.

"The only man of the Congress Party to really attempt to obtain India's independence," Das Gupta would remark.

"One of the World's really great men," Parkash would echo.

In vain, I tried to change the subject, to stem the never-ending flow of oft-repeated remarks, but it was hopeless, so carried away were they with the novelty of the happenings which had raised them from the position of humble clerks to mighty men of valour. As the country closed in about us and we ran through the narrow plain with the Pegu Yomas on our left, and the Shan Hills on our right, I thought that I had successfuly changed the subject; but it was otherwise, and we passed through Thawatti, Pyinmana and Yamethin with their fatuous remarks ringing in my ears.

Came Thazi, Wundwin and Kyaukse, and the country changed to the dry dusty Central Burma semi-desert—and still it went on and on until we came in sight of the mighty Irrawaddy.

It had abated as we made the crossing, and now I felt that it was silenced for ever—and I proved to be right—the period of their disillusionment had begun.

We headed west soon after leaving the river, running more or less parallel to it for some distance, and then turning north-west for the town of Monywa where we were to detrain. The Japanese engine drivers screwed the utmost power out of their engines, fearful of the deadly Beaufighters, and the train bounced and swayed in an alarming fashion. Anyway I was sick of travelling in such a fashion; we were comfortable enough so far as it went, but the feeding arrangements were extremely poor. Every meal, which was cooked in one of the wagons, was the same; rice, pumpkin, and a little meat of doubtful origin, served up in a bowl to be eaten with the fingers. The only beverage available was water, and that was none too clean, and always luke-warm.

As we drew farther away from civilisation, nearer to the wild hills and dense jungle, the spirits of my companions began to droop, even though their fears were temporarily at rest. They had never seen anything like that gloomy jungle, and the sight of it filled them with forebodings for their future comfort. These, sleek, city-bred Indians were to find out many things before they were very much older.

At last we came to Monywa on the Chindwin River, the main Japanese line of communication in that part of Burma, a neat enough little town, and there we detrained. After leaving the train we were marched to a camp overlooking the river for the night. It was better than the nights spent on the train, although not too good by our standards. The I.N.A. officers slept in a *basha,* inferior to the accommodation occupied by the Japanese officers, but infinitely better than that provided for the men.

I went to bed that night wondering what was to come next in this strange adventure of mine.

I FIND AN ALLY

DURING the journey from Rangoon I had noticed a Sikh jemadar; the ranks of the I.N.A. being the same as those of the Indian Army. He was a middle-aged man, with a tinge of grey in his beard, and an impressive row of decorations; most of these were Indian Army decorations which the Japanese, with strange inconsistency, allowed the I.N.A. men to wear. His Long Service Medals told me that he was a regular soldier. He spoke a fair amount of English, and impressed me favourably with his attempts at handling the motley crowd under him. He was the only officer of his grade, and carried out duties roughly equivalent to those of a Sergeant-Major in the British Army. His name, I discovered, was Gurbaksh Singh.

I had just finished my breakfast, the usual depressing concoction of rice, on the morning after our arrival at Monywa, and had walked away from the camp buildings to the edge of the river. I had been there for a few minutes, watching the various types of craft being loaded with supplies for the advancing Japanese forces, when I became aware that I was not alone. I turned round, and there stood Jemadar Gurbaksh Singh. He saluted me gravely, and after a brief hesitation, spoke to me.

"May Sahib please excuse me coming to him like this. Things are not good with me, or with my men; we are unhappy."

As he spoke these words I looked at him narrowly, being well aware of the methods used by the Japanese to obtain recruits for the I.N.A. from amongst the Indian

P.O.W.'s; promises of good treatment and rewards, beatings, starving, and even torture if the men proved obstinate. Then there were the off-hand methods used by the Japanese in dealing with the Indians, and the poor quality and general incompetence of the I.N.A. officers. I was not surprised to learn that the men were discontented, they could hardly be otherwise, and I already had a vague idea that I might be able to put this discontent to good use.

"That is all right, Jemadar Sahib," I said, using the courtesy title which I had noted that the Japanese often omitted to do. "What is wrong?"

He hesitated again, and then glancing over his shoulder to see if we were unobserved, went on in the manner of a man making a sudden plunge.

"I speak to you, Sahib, for you are like my old Sahib in the days before Japanis come. I am a soldier for many years. I have one O.B.I." (Order of British India), said he, pointing to a ribbon on his chest. "Since I go to Rangoon I have not been treated as a soldier. Yesterday one Japani officer slap my face before my men, and my *izat* (self respect) is gone. I speak to the other Sahibs many times, but they do nothing. They are not like my old Sahibs in the Punjab Regiment. So, Sahib, what to do?"

I sized the situation up at once. Here was a man, an old soldier of the best type, a simple loyal man who had been forced or deluded into joining the I.N.A., a man who remembered days when he was a soldier and was treated as one, and had been comparing his present conditions unfavourably with his earlier experiences. It was the opportunity that I had been waiting for. I remembered an incident which had taken place in India when I was there. The Japanese had landed two former Indian Army men whom they had persuaded and trained to become spies from a submarine on the coast of North-West

India. Within a few hours of landing the men had reported to the local Police Station, where they revealed the whole scheme. Yet for a moment or two I hesitated; the man might be indiscreet; then I also took the plunge.

"How did you come to join the I.N.A. Jemadar Sahib?" I asked.

It was his turn to look closely at me, and hesitate before replying.

"I was taken prisoner in Singapore, and spent much time in prison. Food very bad. Many times the I.N.A. Sahibs come to tell us that we can be free, and get much land in India. For a long time I will not join, but then I read that the British Sahibs are all leaving India, and then I join."

He paused again, and looked over his shoulder, then went on:

"There is much I do not understand about you, Sahib. You look like my old Sahibs who are now in prison, and you talk like them, yet you are wearing *dushman* (enemy) uniform, and you are here."

"Sahib," I replied, "you know who I am; everyone here knows who and what I am. How could I be what you say? Are the Japanese fools that they would permit me to be here? Besides which, Sahib, these things you say would not please the Japanese if I told them."

He looked at me without showing a trace of fear for several moments before he replied,

"Sahib," he said at length. "There comes a time when big things become little things. I had thought that I had put away the things of my old life when I joined the I.N.A., but you have brought them back to me, and my mind is not at rest. I have been good Government man all my life. I have heard plenty of Congress wallahs belch out much clever talking that I do not understand; but I do know that they look like the *bania* from the Town who would lend money on my land and then, when I have spent it, come and ask for it back, when he well knows that I have it not, that he may seize my land. My Sahibs always treated me well and I have broken my word by putting on these clothes, Sahib; that is great. Some other things that seemed great now seem small. Sahib, Government was to me *man bap* (Father and Mother) and now I know what lies ahead, and I know not how I shall be rewarded for this mistake I have made. I. . . ."

He stopped talking and eyed me yet more closely.

"Sahib," he continued, "I am a simple man but I have two good eyes; I have seen what I have seen; and I know."

"What do you mean?", I countered.

"This, Sahib! When we were at the Ava Bridge and that aeroplane did blow up the trains I was watching you. I was in the ditch near you with the I.N.A. Sahibs and I saw naught of them but their backsides; but you Sahib went up to the edge and watched and when the engine went 'Whoosh!' you nearly danced for joy, and I thought that you would start and cheer. It was as well that the Japanis were not near to you then and that these other Sahibs did not contemplate as I did. I am but a simple man, but it was written clear upon your face."

I could only stand and stare at him. Finally, I recovered my composure and said,

"What nonsense——"

"Sahib," he cut in gently, "I know; is it not sufficient that I have said nothing of this matter to the Japanis?"

I thought long and hard.

"Sahib," I said. "I look like a British Sahib, and I talk like one, because I am one. I cannot tell you everything, for I should be shot at once if the Japanis knew this. You must trust me. I can tell you though that the

British are not leaving India, and even now many of them are behind the Japanese lines killing the Japanese."

"Sahib. Sahib," he said. "These Japanis are but foolish men, if they do not know that you are British. Yet it is good."

"Do your men feel as you feel?"

"Some of them, Sahib, those that were Sepoys before; but I have some low caste men from Rangoon." At this he spat expressively upon the ground. "They are not soldiers; they are but coolies who were put amongst us. But Sahib they are very frightened now."

"Now," I said, "I can do nothing to help you yet, but soon I may be able to get you back to your old regiment. You must not be seen speaking to me often or someone will become suspicious. You must also be very careful of what you say to your men; speak only a few words to the men you know and trust, and warn them also to be careful. Say nothing to these men from Rangoon. Now you must go, and remember what I have said, but be very careful."

His bearded face broke into a broad grin, and, after saluting me, he walked away. I stayed where I was for some time, lost in thought. About eighty of his men were real soldiers, and almost all of them must have been recruited in a similar manner. I had no doubt of what they would do if they were given a lead at the right moment. It was distinctly encouraging. Untold difficulties might lie ahead, but I need not face them alone if I played my cards properly. Nothing could be done yet; I could only wait for the time when I was expected to put on my guide act. Somehow or other I was going to put a spoke into this carefully-laid scheme.

Then I returned to the camp where I found preparations being made for another move. In the confusion I slipped up to Captain Ghosh, and engaged him in conversation about general matters. Whilst we were talking the jemadar came past, and I made a casual remark to Ghosh:

"A fine looking man, the jemadar."

The reply was thoroughly typical of the man.

"Hmm, perhaps he is, but he is not good soldier."

I walked away too full for words.

Very soon after this little incident we were marched down to the landing stage, for the next part of the journey was to be made by boat up the Chindwin River to Kalewa at the bottom end of the dreaded Kabaw Valley. As I marched along I surveyed the streets and houses of the little town of Monywa, and I wondered how long it would be before I lived in a civilised house again—if ever.

The riverside was a scene of tremendous activity, and all sizes and shapes of boats were being loaded. I saw one or two flat-bottomed river steamers, remnants of the Irrawaddy Flotilla Company's fleet, and the mast of several others out in the stream marked where they had been sunk in the 1942 retreat. The great majority of the boats however, were Country boats and *sampans* of various kinds; some large, and some small, and all with the characteristic high stern and lateen sail of the ordinary native craft. Most of them had engines as well as the large single sail to help them against the strong current of the river.

At one jetty, coolies were loading bags of rice, at another, boxes of ammunition were going on board, a large number of mules were waiting to be loaded, a number of tankettes and three-ton vehicles were going on to some of the larger vessels, and, at yet another jetty, drums of petrol were being loaded. An atmosphere of suppressed excitement hung over the broad sunlit river, the men were working with tremendous energy to ensure that their rapidly-advancing Army should not lack supplies.

The news that morning had been good—for the Japanese. Imphal was surrounded, and some two hundred thousand British and Indian troops trapped—according to the Japanese. The Force was in high spirits, feeling themselves to be on the crest of a wave that would carry them to victory and even my friends, Parkash, Ghosh, and Das Gupta, had shaken off their gloomy forebodings. The 'March on Delhi' had begun, and it was confidently expected that the task that lay ahead would prove to be a relatively simple one.

There was some delay at the landing stage, and so the opportunity was taken to deliver a pep talk to the Force. Major Tagachaki harangued the Japanese, and Colonel Mohindar Singh did likewise to the Indians. I understood little of what was being said, but it appeared that the troops were being promised leave in Calcutta in two months time!

As the spirits of the enemy went up, so mine descended in inverse proportion; and, as doubts began to strike me, I wondered if my careful scheming would come to naught after all. It is easy to laugh at enemy propaganda when other and more reliable sources of information are available, but when it is the only source of news it is difficult not to be influenced by it. Suppose the Japanese were as successful as they claimed to be? That they were having some success was evident, and they had an impressive record of success behind them. Suppose they did succeed in cutting the vital Assam Railway as a preliminary to over-running the whole of the province of Assam? I did not need to be much of a strategist to see that the cutting of the railway would mean the evacuation of the whole of Assam, and the abandonment of the great airfields from which supplies of war material were flown to China. The construction of the Ledo Road would be stopped; and the position of the two Chinese Divisions on the Northern Front, and that of our own Chindits then operating in the Katha-Indaw-Maulu triangle, far in the rear of the Jap lines, would become desperate.

Then I was worried about my revelations to the old jemadar; indiscreet ones I feared, for if things went well for the Japanese he might be tempted to think again. It hung over me during the whole of the journey from Monywa to Kalewa, and I went in constant fear of my life on this score. From the foregoing it may be gathered that I was in a thoroughly unenviable frame of mind. The things that worried me most of all, however, were some disquieting visions of myself marching through the streets of New Delhi as an officer of the I.N.A. to be decorated and rewarded for the part that I had played in the 'March on Delhi'.

The boats turned up at last, ten of them, and we embarked, fifty men to each boat; I was pleased to find that the I.N.A. element travelled in separate boats, I felt safer that way. It was quite a large craft that I travelled on, although none too big for fifty men and a large cargo of rice, on the piled-up bags of which we slept during the night we spent on board. The boat was powered by two ordinary truck engines set amidships driving a single screw, and these provided sufficient power for a speed of about three or four knots against the fast-flowing current.

The boats travelled in a convoy, constantly hugging one bank or the other, so that they might quickly gain the shelter of the overhanging trees in case of air attack. That this was no idle fear was proved soon after we left Monywa. One of the boats had lagged behind, because of slight engine trouble, and in an effort at overtaking the other boats had cut across a bend of the river instead of following the sweep of the outside bank. A sudden roar of engines sent nine of the boats heading for the cover of the trees and safety. The tenth boat out in midstream also turned for the bank, but at the crucial moment one of the engines began to misfire badly, and it was much too slow for the deadly Beaufighter swooping out of the blue sky. I caught a glimpse of the red and blue roundels on the green-gray wings, and then the guns began to rattle, and the little spouts of water kicked up by the bullets rushed towards the boat. Without any warning whatever, there was a thunderous roar which echoed and re-echoed around the hills, the boat disappeared in a blinding flash, and a thick black column of smoke mushroomed upwards. Pieces of debris splashed into the water around us, and we were near enough to feel the blast from the explosion like the buffetting of a giant hand. The Beaufighter also had been near enough to feel the effect of the explosion, indeed it rocked so violently that I thought it would dive into the river; but it recovered and disappeared at tree top height as quickly as it had come. The boat, and its miserable occupants, had vanished without trace, apart from a few floating fragments of timber, and I conjecture that it had been carrying a cargo of explosives, or possibly shells, which had been exploded by the Beaufighter's fire. Anyway, fifty Japanese were no longer interested in the 'March on Delhi'.

This little incident cheered me considerably—at least the R.A.F. were still active—but it had precisely the reverse effect upon Ghosh who was travelling in the same boat as myself, coming as such an unpleasant reminder of the similar occurrence at Ava, and just at a time when he was feeling elated by the good news. How strange it was that yet another British plane had escaped the wholesale destruction to which the R.A.F. had been subjected! I did nothing to comfort the poor man, and it is scarcely surprising that his fears grew stronger, as he witnessed the dreadful state of terror to which his fellow-officer and travelling companion had been reduced!

We saw no more action during the trip, although I thought I heard the distant chatter of machine gun fire an hour or so after the attack. If someone else was the target I was glad, for it is not pleasant to act the part of clay pigeon, even when one realised that the enemy is discomforted thereby.

For hour after hour the boats glided along on the broad face of the Chindwin, past an occasional island, and always with the green wall of the jungle looming thick and dark on either bank, and the distant hills growing steeper, wilder, and more forbidding with each passing mile. Now and then a little village swam into view; little clusters of bamboo *bashas* built on short piles, with the small plot of cultivated land carved out of the jungle, and the crazy bamboo landing stage at the water's edge. Perhaps a few dug-outs or other craft would be moored thereto, each with a pair of eyes painted on the bows—to enable the boat to see its way. Sometimes we passed a flotilla of empty boats sailing in the opposite direction, assisted, as we were impeded, by the fast flowing river, and occasionally a few boats that were not empty, the still, bandaged forms lying on the decks proving that the campaign was no walk-over for the Japanese.

Night fell; the silver bosom of the river became a seemingly solid bed of smooth black pitch, and the wall of the jungle the sides of a deep black canyon, with the bright stars gleaming overhead. With the coming of darkness the stillness of that remote and solitary place became oppressive, despite the splutter of the engine exhausts, a sound which scarcely caused a ripple on the great still lake of silence; and a great feeling of loneliness fell upon me. I was there, far away from my kith and kin, with none to whom I could turn for a word of advice, and I felt the weight of the great responsibility that was upon my shoulders. For all that I knew to the contrary, upon my actions of the next few weeks, or even days, depended the failure or success of an attempt at cutting that most vital line of communication, the railway, at a time when the whole trend of the war in Asia trembled in the balance. I remember resting my head in my hands whilst a wave of black depression swept over me. How could my feeble efforts make the slightest difference, one way or the other?

I expected that we should stop for the night somewhere, but that was not the case, and we continued our journey in the middle of the river now that there was no danger of aerial attack. I fell asleep with the mood of black depression still upon me, and the ripple of water, and the chug of the engines in my ears.

We reached Kalewa at the confluence of the Chindwin and Myittha rivers on the afternoon of the following day. As the little fleet of boats chugged up to the landing stages, I saw that Kalewa itself was little more than a name, or to be more accurate it had been, before the Japanese had turned it into an advanced Base Camp. When I saw it, it was a small township of bamboo *bashas*, large and small, concealed as far as possible beneath the trees. Here were the dumps of stores, accumulated during the weeks preceding the opening of the offensive, and food, ammunition and stocks of the thousand and one articles needed to sustain a modern army.

I don't know what it was that gave me the idea, perhaps it was the sight of so much dry bamboo, and dry bamboo is very inflammable once it is alight. It doesn't matter very much now, but it did occur to me then that a match, judiciously applied, would do a lot towards helping the Allied War Effort.

As we disembarked, and marched to the camp where we were to stay for two days to pick up our equipment, I kept my eyes open. The rough earth road led between a number of large buildings near to the river, but there were numerous sentries stationed at every vantage point, and too much water in the river for fire-fighting purposes, so I dismissed the idea from my mind.

The camp needs no description. It was like all the other camps that I had seen previously, and it is sufficient to say that we officers were housed much more comfortably than the men again, but very much less so than the Japanese officers.

The issue of the various items of equipment was planned to take place on the following day, and so, after I had settled myself in, I took a walk round the camp to familiarise myself with the geography of the place. A fence surrounded the camp, and I noticed that there were six very large *bashas* in a compound behind our camp, and a road led up to this compound from the main road which ran along the front of the camp. I wondered what this place could be, for numerous three-ton lorries laden with sacks of some commodity were bumping up and down the road to this compound in a constant stream. However, I soon discovered what these lorries carried as one passed me leaving behind it a thin trail of rice pouring from a torn sack on the back. So that was it—rice—the main food of the Japanese.

That set me thinking again. There were six of the buildings, each two hundred feet in length and fifty feet in width. If they were full of rice, then they contained a lot of rice, enough to feed a large number of men for many days. Suppose one of the buildings should catch fire? The bamboo walls would burn readily, and so would the rice inside, but not so readily as the thatched roof. The winter rains had ceased, and everything was as dry as a bone.

That was all very fine, but it was not so easy to see how it could be accomplished. Without doubt, sentries would be posted at night, and fire points established inside the compound for dealing with just such an outbreak; but I did notice that the *bashas* had been built a little too closely together for safety. I stood pondering the matter for some time, thinking what a good thing it would be if I could destroy those stocks of rice. Had not Napoleon stated that every army marched upon its stomach? If only I could destroy that rice I might be the means of holding back the Japanese advance, for a few days at any rate. I thought of climbing the fence when it was dark, running the gauntlet of the sentries, and simply applying a match to the inflammable thatch; unfortunately though, I would be detected when I tried to make my getaway, if not before. That didn't seem to be good enough.

The nearest *basha* was separated from the fence dividing the two compounds by a distance of about twenty yards, and that was the nearest that I could get to them. The fence was about seven feet in height, and composed of stout wooden posts and runners to which *chattai* matting (strong matting made of closely woven split bamboo) was tied, making a fence through which it was difficult to see, but which was by no means unclimbable despite the few strands of barbed wire strung along the top.

Whilst I was wandering around thinking the matter over, an idea occurred to me, which I at first brushed aside as being too wildly improbable. I had noticed a number of large rat traps, of the wire cage and spring-loaded trap door variety, which effectively imprison the rat, but leave it quite uninjured. On inspecting the traps I discovered that three of them were inhabited, each by a savage looking rodent as large as a small cat, which looked at me with beady, unwinking eyes, as I thoughtfully contemplated the manner of their segregation. Having made sure that I was unobserved, I opened one of the traps to see what would happen. Sure enough, as soon as the trap was opened, out bounded the occupant, and, in the twinkling of an eye, it darted across the intervening space to the fence, and disappeared through a hole at the bottom in the direction of the nearest large *basha*.

The idea, childish as it seemed, germinated in my brain, and as soon as it was really dark I decided to make the attempt. Whilst in Rangoon, I had purchased a small brass cigarette lighter, together with a bottle containing about a quarter of a pint of lighter fluid. After hunting about I found some pieces of coarse string, left behind by the thatchers when they thatched the roofs in the camp. These I tied together until they measured about twenty feet in length, and about eighteen inches from one end I attached a short piece of wire. Then I took my handkerchief and rolled it into a ball, as tightly as I could, and fastened it to the end of the piece of wire. My preparations were nearly complete. In the other end of the piece of string I made a running noose, with a thumb knot as a stop to prevent the noose from being drawn up tight.

I concealed all these articles in my pockets, and, having made sure that no curious eyes were upon me, I made my way to the fence. After dumping the various articles I crept away and secured one of the rat traps complete with rat. The beast scuffled about a bit as I carried it along, and its faint scratching sounded like the beat of a horse's hooves to my keyed-up consciousness. I felt sure that the noise could be heard a hundred yards away. However I reached the spot that I had selected without the alarm being raised.

First of all I crouched down on the inside of the fence, listening to the movements of the sentry on the other side. So far as I could make out, he patrolled the whole length of the fence; up, right alongside the fence; and down, on the other side of the *bashas*. That suited me very nicely; there would be a period of about three minutes when he was completely out of sight of the fence. I carefully laid the trap on the ground with the door directly opposite the hole, and just a few inches away. Then I coiled the string carefully, so that it would uncoil without tangling, and fixed it with the noose over the hole in the fence. I poured the lighter fluid over the handkerchief. In one hand I held the end of the string, and in the other my cigarette lighter. I was ready.

I listened carefully until I heard the sentry pass by, then I waited a little until I judged that he had turned round the end of the *bashas*, risking that he had not stopped somewhere in sight of the stretch of fence behind which I lay. That was a risk that had to be taken anyway. In any case I should soon find out when I flicked the lighter—there would be silence—or——. With a quick movement, I opened the trap and, just as I had calculated, the hungry rat made a beeline for home, food and safety, or in other words the nearest rice *basha*, by way of the hole in the bottom of the fence. There was a sharp scuffle of paws, and then it was away through the hole—and the noose—and in a brief space of time I was holding the very end of the string, with the rat tugging at the other end. The wire with the pad attached was on the other side of the fence, and it was but the work of a moment to reach through the hole with my right hand, and flick the lighter under the petrol-soaked handkerchief, at the same time releasing the string with my left hand. It was done; and I caught a brief glimpse of a flash of flame through the interstices of the *chattai,* and then it was gone —and so was I!

I put as great a distance between myself and that fence in the shortest space of time that I could possibly manage, without making my haste too obvious, and within two minutes I was strolling casually into the hut where the other I.N.A. officers were sitting, hoping that my appearance was quite normal, Apparently it was, for no comment was made. Then I sat and waited, trying to picture what was happening:—if anything. One of two things could happen; the rat would either stop inside the hut somewhere where the pad would burn itself out harmlessly, or dive behind or under the sacks of rice, dragging the flaming ball behind it. It all depended upon the rat going deep enough to drag the twenty feet of string right beneath the sacks. If the fire started at all, it should start in a place where it could not be detected until it had gained a firm hold.

The time passed by on leaden wings, and nothing seemed to be happening, so that I began to think my attempt had failed. I consulted my watch at frequent intervals, and I have never known the hands move so slowly. After nearly twenty minutes had elapsed, I came to the conclusion that it really was no go, and I felt very disappointed because my scheming had come to naught; but just as I was putting my watch away there was a loud shout from outside, followed by the loud clanging of a gong.

I rushed outside with the others:—and there it was, exactly as I had hoped. Even as I gazed, the inflammable thatch on the roof of the burning *basha* burst into a sheet of flame, and in a very brief space of time the *basha* was an inferno; the flimsy roof collapsed, and the red flames and billowing black smoke leaped skywards.

A light breeze was blowing, carrying showers of sparks over the other *bashas*, and suddenly to my great delight the thatch of the next hut took fire, the flames running from end to end with astonishing rapidity, until that too was well alight. Then another, another, until they all were a roaring mass of flame.

I could have danced for joy, but I restrained myself, and hurried to the scene of the outbreak with the others, ostensibly to assist, but actually to hinder, if that was possible. The intervening fence was pushed over, and, within a few more minutes, water was being thrown on to the flames. I was glad to see that this had little effect. A truck, drawing a trailer pump, rattled up, and a determined effort was made to control the flames.

After a while the flames were brought under control, and little by little reduced to a smoking blackened heap, bearing little resemblance to the six large *bashas* that had formerly stood there. I would have preferred to have seen the rice totally destroyed, but, even so, I could not imagine how anyone could possibly eat any of that soaked, and charred stuff. Perhaps a few sound bags were eventually salvaged from beneath the heaps, but it could have been very little.

I went to bed that night feeling that I had accomplished something worthwhile. The future was all unknown, but I was not despondent as I had been on the previous night.

COMFORT PLATOONS

IN the morning the Japanese held a Court of Inquiry at the scene of the fire; and I watched the proceedings, which were presided over by a fierce little major supported by two lieutenants, with the greatest of interest. The witnesses consisted exclusively of the guard, and they were lined up under escort, which seemed to show that they alone were suspected. The possible implications of an outside agency seemed not to have been considered; but it was scarcely surprising since my incendiary device would have vanished without a trace.

The men of the guard were questioned one by one; a good deal of face slapping being used as a spur to their memories, and one unfortunate individual received special attention. He must have been the sentry on duty at the time of the outbreak. His face was smacked so long and heartily that he could not have been capable of a single logical thought; at any rate he was led away under arrest when his interrogation came to an end, having apparently failed to satisfy the Court. After that the Court broke up, and that was the end of the matter so far as I was concerned—or so I thought at the time.

Whilst this was going on, the rest of the Force were extremely busy drawing equipment of various kinds, having travelled from Rangoon with nothing but rifles and light automatics. Ammunition of all sizes was served out, and the heavier weapons collected. These consisted of a number of mortars and four mule guns, which were handy pack guns firing a 75 mm. shell, capable of no great range or accuracy, but extremely effective at short ranges. Besides these were anti-tank mines of the usual Japanese pattern, and a quantity of explosives. Being a Sapper, I was particularly interested in the latter, some of which I managed to examine, discovering that it was picric acid cast into small blocks covered with waxed paper. I hadn't had much experience with picric acid, but I knew that it was roughly equal in power to our own guncotton.

All these stores and weapons were to be carried by mules, in the same way as they were carried in Wingate's outfit, but we did not collect them there and then, since they had been taken forward as far as Tamu, and we should collect them when we arrived there. The stores and men were to be taken to Tamu by truck through the Kabaw Valley; although it had at first been intended that they should march, for the Japanese had little transport to spare; but the speed with which the offensive had thus far moved had made it imperative to move the special troops forward as rapidly as possible.

I took no part in this packing and unpacking, nor in loading the stores on to the trucks; I was merely the guide, and as such almost completely ignored, a state of affairs which suited me very well, but I was pleased when I was given a long-barrelled automatic pistol of 7 mm. calibre, and sixty rounds of ammunition. It was good to feel the butt of such a useful weapon again.

At length the day drew to a close, all being ready for the start on the following morning.

I was sitting in the I.N.A. Officers' hut thinking as usual, when the tired Indians came in. They had had a trying day; the arrangements connected with issuing equipment to the I.N.A. troops had not gone at all smoothly, and there had been some overbearing interference on the part of some of the Japanese officers who could not tolerate such a chaotic state of affairs. Despite this, they were in a good humour, and I ventured to ask Ghosh why he was looking so pleased.

"Don't you know?" he answered, "We have just been told that we are to have a visit from two Comfort Platoons tonight. This is our last night here, and we are getting this as a reward for the important task we are undertaking."

So that was it! This careful attention to the sexual needs of the Japanese troops surprised me, despite the many stories that I had heard. A completely matter of fact view was taken of the whole business, and a man was provided with a woman at intervals, just as he was supplied with food and clothing; and that was all there was to it.

I awaited the arrival of the Comfort girls with some interest—perhaps I should say with great interest. This was something new to me. This was just plain sex—without trimmings.

At half-past seven they arrived in three lorries which drove in through the entrance where I was standing, and stopped just inside the gates. As soon as the engines were switched off, I could hear the occupants of the vehicles chattering and giggling like so many parrots. Evidently they did not resent being Comfort girls. In any case I suppose that they had mostly been recruited from amongst the numerous prostitute population of some large Eastern city. No doubt, some few of them had been collected locally by fair means or foul, but even so they would soon have been completely demoralised by the other women, prostitutes of the lowest class. In any case the Eastern attitude towards prostitution is very different from our own.

The lorry tail boards were lowered, and out they all jumped, to stand in a chattering group, unabashed by the staring eyes around them. Most of them were low-class

Koreans, with lank black hair, indifferent figures, and flat, almost vacant, faces. They wore gaily-coloured *lungyis* and blouses, their lips painted a vivid red, and their faces were daubed with powder in the crudest manner imaginable. There was also a sprinkling of Chinese women dressed in extremely short coloured frocks, painted in a positively hideous fashion; cheeks dead white under a dense layer of powder, mouths a gash of red, with dead black eyebrows painted in the most impossible positions, and wearing ridiculously high-heeled shoes.

A small group of girls of a rather better appearance stood a little part from the others. Their dress was neater, they were better looking, and their make-up was applied more sparingly and with a little more artistry. They were the officers' girls.

I counted about sixty women altogether, and as the Force numbered about five hundred men all told, a rough calculation showed that each of the common women was expected to deal with about ten men: assuming that there would be no abstainers. A similar calculation showed that each officers' woman had to 'entertain' four officers. I suppose that it is difficult for the average decent man or woman to visualise such a state of affairs, such vile degradation of a normal function of humanity. Ten men in as many hours! Perhaps as many as two hundred different men in one month!

Three huts had been prepared for the events of the evening and, as I watched the women made their way to these huts, laughing and talking as they went, I was so completely fascinated by these unusual happenings that I followed behind. A long queue of men was already waiting outside the huts, exactly like the queue for a cinema performance, and a few N.C.O's maintained order.

As the women approached, the men became excited, and surged forward, only to be pushed back by the N.C.O's and the air was filled with their shouts and what were, I suppose, catcalls. A more animal-like demonstration I have never seen in the whole of my life. Yet the women were not one whit disconcerted, answering the yells with shrill squeals, making improper gestures, and one abandoned creature even went so far as to lift her skirts above her waist to expose the whole of the lower part of her body. Near to the huts they divided into three groups, and made their way inside, one group to each hut, hurrying past the yelling men still laughing and chattering.

Meanwhile the officers' girls had been led away in the direction of the officers' quarters, walking quietly as if to show that they were superior to the other women. I let them go without much interest. I was too busy watching the incredible scene before me, and in any case I had no designs upon any of them.

It was quite dark, but the three huts were lighted inside, and I drew nearer to catch a glimpse of the interior, into which I could see very easily now that the queue of men had been pushed to one side. The huts had been roughly curtained off into cubicles, each containing a rough *charpoy* (bed), but the screening was done so carelessly that it was possible to see into many of them. Apparently concealment was no consideration. In each of the cubicles was a women preparing herself for the handling that she was about to receive. Most of them removed all their clothes in a quite open fashion, and I could see them running from one cubicle to the other wearing not a stitch of clothing. Occasionally one would come to the door to exhibit herself and make inviting gestures to the wildly excited men.

At last they were all ready, and the Master of Ceremonies, one of the Jap N.C.O's, allowed the first batch of men to approach the *bashas*. They did not enter immediately, but proceeded to wash themselves at a row of metal bowls set by the door, clearly as a precaution against the transmission of V.D. I was to see later that they repeated this performance after they left the building at the end of their 'session'. The Japanese authorities were aware then of the danger of wholesale outbreaks of V.D., and took the elementary precaution of arranging matters so that every man washed himself with some disinfectant solution before and after intercourse.

Then they rushed into the huts, pushing and jostling one another in their efforts to get into the cubicles containing the more desirable women, and the orgy began.

I stood watching until I was sickened by what I saw. The men came and went at regular intervals; twenty minutes was the period allowed to each; and, if at the end of that time a man had not left voluntarily, a shrill scream from the woman brought an N.C.O. to the cubicle and the man was forcibly removed. This happened but seldom; usually the women, with a dexterity born of long practice succeeded in satisfying the demands made upon them in a very short time. It was the same thing over and over again. On entering the cubicle the man would find the woman sitting or lying on the bed. After removing some of his clothing he would sit by her side, and she, putting her arms around him, would make a few mechanical and perfunctory gestures of mock endearment, stroking his face and kissing him on the lips. If that did not suffice she would go to the extreme in her efforts at stimulating his lusts, and within a few minutes it was all over, and the man rising from the bed, would dress and go out, leaving the woman to make some small attempt at straightening her tangled hair, repairing her smeared make-up, and otherwise making herself ready for the next man. Then she assumed the same attitude on the bed, the next man came in, and the same sordid performance was repeated. The large queue outside quietened down, and soon they were waiting their turn, squatting on the ground with true Oriental patience, and the business began to go like clockwork.

A feeling of utter revulsion swept over me like a wave, leaving behind it a sense of contamination so that I felt degraded myself by what I had seen. It came without warning; at one moment I was still amazed and interested, and then all at once I could not bear the sight of those abandoned creatures dealing with man after man, young and middle-aged, tall and short, fat and thin, any and anything, with less discrimination than a bitch on heat at a street corner. Perhaps it was the openness with which it was carried out; for the faintly attractive aura of mystery and naughtiness which is usually associated with the activities of ladies of easy virtue was absent. They were so utterly without shame that they would, I am quite sure, have done what they were doing on a stage before a crowd of spectators. Mere machines, reduced to a state far lower than that of any animal, empty hulks devoid of all purpose and meaning beyond that of being used and used over and over again. This was evil in the absolute, carried to that ultimate degree of perfection below which there are no lower depths to plumb, and wickedness itself becomes endued with a peculiar quality of stultified innocence.

I hurried away as if the devil himself was behind me—perhaps that was the case—and made my way to my *basha*, quite forgetting that it was likely that similar things were happening there. I was sharing a hut with my old friends, Ghosh, Parkash, and Das Gupta, and usually at that time of the night an oil lamp would be burning, but I found the place in darkness. All the other living huts were also dark, but a blaze of light and shouts of laughter from the large building which was used as a Mess, told me that the officers were being entertained by the girls. I had no desire whatever to see what was happening. I had seen enough of prostitution that one night to satisfy me for a long time, and I wanted no more of it even though it might be covered with a thin veneer of decorum. I was about to strike a match when I heard one of the beds creak slightly, followed by a smothered feminine laugh. That told me everything. One of the others had a woman in there. I almost fled from the hut, feeling worse than ever, and walked under the stars until my outraged senses returned to something like normal again. It was growing late, and as I was beginning to feel sleepy I returned to the *basha*, which I found to my great relief, to be apparently empty. I undressed without investigating too closely, and I was soon beneath my mosquito net wooing sleep, a much more attractive proposition than indulging in commercialised love with the Comfort girls, and within a short time I was in the friendly arms of Morpheus.

I had little time to marvel at the happenings of the previous night when we started very early next morning, but I can remember that it seemed like a dream; but the rows of metal bowls still standing outside the *bashas* served to convince me of the reality of the naked whores who had plied their trade in those huts on the previous night.

We were loaded into a fleet of trucks which was standing waiting, and bumped out of the camp on to the rutty earth road, bound for Tamu by way of the Kabaw Valley. It was the real start of the expedition, just as the departure from the Nam Yung bridge had been the real beginning of my own column's activities. It seemed so strange, almost unbelievable, to realise that only a few weeks previously I was plodding up the Ledo Road, southward bound, in company with a bunch of bearded desperados. Then I had no idea of what awaited me; certainly I had not expected that I should penetrate to the very heart of enemy occupied territory, to be accepted as an enemy agent, and then find myself a member of a very similar raiding party northward bound, bent upon spreading the same terror and confusion behind the British Lines as my comrades were even then spreading behind the Japanese lines.

The two forces contrasted oddly: in one the men were white and bearded; in the other, neglecting the I.N.A. element they were sallow and smooth-faced. The Wingate force was heading into Burma with little but a sorry record of defeat to the credit of British Arms in Burma; whereas the Japanese force was going forward on the crest of a wave of success. One force was composed of grumbling, cursing, sceptical Englishmen, Welsh, Scots and Irish; the other of chattering fanatical Japanese; both island races, one from the East and one from the West.

The similarities were as marked as the differences: both were tough, well-armed, and disciplined, similarly equipped and trained, and could be depended upon to give an account of themselves in a tight corner, but there was one very great difference. The British force was of homogenous construction, excepting the small Burmese *recce* platoon, whilst the Japanese force was only two-thirds Japanese and reliable; the I.N.A. portion, composed and officered as it was, being of extremely doubtful value. Furthermore, the Japanese were relying unbeknown to them, upon a guide of indeterminate potentiality in the shape and person of myself—alias Maurice Derocque, Capt. I.N.A.

Just as we left Monywa after receiving good news of the Japanese advance, that is, good for the Japanese, so did we leave Kalewa. The offensive was continuing, and a very large stretch of the Manipur Road right down as far as Kohima was in the hands of the Japanese. The Naga village of Kohima was expected to fall at any time, leaving the road open for the advance upon the Base Camp of Dimapur—and the railway.

No doubt some of the claims were premature or exaggerated, but I had no means of knowing, and it is a fact that the Japs did suceed in cutting the road from Imphal to Kohima at about that time, reaching the last-named place where they ran into determined resistance. Kohima, the tiny township and the site of a Convalescent Depot, saw some of the bloodiest fighting of the whole campaign as the crack Japanese 31st Division flung itself, in vain, upon a scratch garrison composed of various remnants and the staff and inmates of the Convalescent Depot. For days the struggle raged fiercely, the District Commissioner's tennis court becoming famous as one of the most fiercely contested spots, whilst desperate efforts were made by the British to bring up reinforcements from India, and the famous British Second Division was despatched from Western India. Imphal, capital of the state of Manipur, was well and truly surrounded and, if the Japanese had succeeded in reaching the railway at any point, the situation for the great body of troops trapped in the Imphal plain would have become well nigh desperate, despite the amazing feats of air-supply and reinforcement, when one whole Division was flown from the Arakan, and the lumbering Dakotas appeared with their supplies at regular intervals.

That was the set-up when we left Kalewa; and, just as I was unaware of the precise nature of events in the struggle, so were the British commanders unaware that a small Task Force was moving up rapidly to attempt to by-pass the block at Kohima, strike for the railway at an unexpected spot to the east of Dimapur, and then, using the facilities offered by a treacherous Indian, appear to the west of Dimapur to halt or hinder the arrival of the urgently-needed reinforcements, thus enabling the main

Japanese body to overwhelm the garrison at Kohima, and reach the railway in great force. Truly the turn of events was balanced upon a knife edge.

All the time that I had been travelling up from Rangoon I had never ceased to marvel because the Indian, from whom I had obtained the Buddha, had not communicated the true state of affairs to his Japanese employers. I have mentioned this in the earlier part of my account and considered several possible explanations. Perhaps the Burman had dropped the statuette after the Indian had handed it to him and the latter had not realised in the haste of his getaway that it had been dropped at all; then, finding that he was not pursued, and no enquiries were made, he would eventually have become quite certain that everything had gone as planned. It was also very likely that he had been informed through secret channels, that the special messenger had arrived safely in Rangoon, never dreaming of the true identity of that messenger. The only man, apart from myself, who could have told the true story was somewhere in the wilds, perhaps dead, or too frightened to carry on with what he had started, fearful both of leaving his column, and of reporting to the Japanese without the Buddha.

LITERARY INTERVIEW

IT is difficult to know people, and I don't think one can ever really know any but one's own countrymen. Men—and I exclude the unknowable women—are not only just themselves, they are also all that has gone into the making of them; the environment in which they were born, the town they lived in, the games they played as children, the schools they attended, the food they ate, the clothes they wore, the books they read, and the God they believed in. It is these things working together that have made them what they are, and these are things that you can't just read about, you can only know them if you have lived them. It follows therefore, that you cannot know any persons of a foreign nation since you cannot have done all the things that they have done; but you can, I suppose, if you have lived amongst them, come to know something of the inner forces that make them do this and do that, when faced with a given set of circumstances.

It is true to say that the cruelties which the Japanese perpetrated during the War fairly curdled the blood of many civilized people. The evils of the German concentration camps were horrible enough, but there was something quite frightening in the barbarities of the Japanese for the simple reason that they were to the Westerner almost unknowable. I can well remember later in the War being at Dimapur and being told that in such and such a compound the Military Police had three Japanese prisoners. It was an event: it was something to talk about in the Mess at night, for the Japanese did not allow themselves to be taken often. They fought almost without reward. They fought without giving or seeking quarter. There seemed to many to be no way to explain the incredible things that the Japanese did except to conclude that they were in some ways warped mentally.

If I have in my narrative made comparatively little of this side of things it is only because I wished to make it reasonably simple and straightforward; not because I never thought of it. It was with me from the very first day that I fell into their hands and, when I could manage to thrust personal considerations to one side, I often pondered these things, and discovered, to my surprise, that many of their actions were the logical outcome of who and what they were.

I shall mention later the Kudan shrine to which the Japanese believed that the spirits of the dead soldiers were transported. I learned that there is near Tokyo, on a hill called Kudan, a Shinto shrine called the Yasukimi Shrine; and the Shinto priests taught, and the Japanese fully believed, that these departed spirits actually hovered there in a sort of heaven-on-earth. It was only necessary for the soldier as he died in battle to call on the name of the Emperor, and he automatically became one of the blessed. The Emperor himself as the Head of the State and the Chief Priest of the Shinto religion was regarded as being more than human. The whole fabric of the Japanese society was, despite all their outward progress, distinctly feudal and authoritarian; the supreme virtue rigid adherence to a tight code of laws and behaviour patterns. Victory was automatic; no Shinto war could end in defeat, and honourable suicide the only possible way to atone for failure. The national code of ethics stated that man's highest goal was unthinking loyalty to his superior and to a code of behaviour rigidly laid down: and that was all.

We are apt to underestimate the profound influence

that Christianity has had upon our outlook and whole way of life. The Christian teaching that our basic moral duty is towards Christ, that in God's eyes all men are equal, and that man's highest good is found in the denial of self, has moulded us and made us what we are—and it is quite different from what the Shinto religion has made the Japanese.

The minds of the Japanese soldiers had been coarsened, in their recruit days, by brutal treatment; the private soldier beaten by everyone in authority above him was in turn utterly merciless to all who fell into his hands. The constant propaganda of duty and devotion to the Emperor produced a highly efficient infantry soldier ready to take part in frenzied bayonet charges, ready to blow himself to pieces as a human land mine, or dive a veritable piloted flying bomb on to the deck of an enemy warship without a qualm, and capable when the tight rein of discipline was slackened of perpetrating the most unmentionable barbarities, without a single qualm of conscience. Of these things, as the days passed by, I became more and more aware and, with this broadening comprehension, there grew within me that profound respect for the Japanese as a fighting man, and a horror, a feeling that this thing was going to sweep across the civilised areas of the world, even as in earlier times the Mongol hordes had swept from the innermost parts of Central Asia, and blot out all that was noble and worthwhile.

Several of the Japanese officers in the Force spoke English, and this language was in fact the vehicle of communication between the Japanese and the Indians. The Force Commander, Major Tagachaki Hideki, or to anglicise it: Major Hideki Tagachaki, could speak fairly good English, and on several occasions held quite lengthy conversations with me. There was always something very unreal and more than a little frightening about these conversations, for, although he addressed me by my assumed French name, he spoke to me as to an Englishman: of that there was no doubt. He was always the same; bland, smiling, often verbose, very well informed, and with an undefinable something which indicated the presence of a set of very sharp claws inside a velvet paw. I have no doubt that he had been one of the many Japanese trade representatives who had visited, amongst other places, England in the thirties, negotiating the flood of textiles, machinery and cheap consumer goods which had been poured out of Japanese ports into the world's trading centres; and in preparation for his mission had acquired a thick superficial coating of Western culture.

I remember one particular conversation with Major Tagachaki,—although I cannot remember exactly where it took place, frightening as it was—which serves to illustrate the fundamental difference in outlook between ourselves and the Japanese.

"Good evening, Derocque," he began, "our journey goes well does it not? You see how expeditiously Japan Forces advance towards their objective. So we go forward to Hakko Ichiyu."

"Hakko Ichiyu, Major Tagachaki?" I replied warily. "You must forgive me but I do not understand."

"Of course not, Derocque; it is not to be expected that you would. I will translate it—'the four corners of the earth under one roof'. It is ancient honourable Japanese slogan. My men sing:

See, the sky opens before the Eastern Sea,
The Rising Sun climbs higher, radiant in its flight.
The Spirit of Heaven and Earth is throbbing with vigour,
And hope dances through the eight islands of Japan . . .
With an unbroken line of Emperors

We are blessed with light and eternity.
We the people, all of us,
Conforming to the Divine Mission of the Virtue of His Imperial Majesty,
Go forth to make the eight corners of the World our home. . . ."

He stopped talking and beamed upon me.

"Perhaps you do not appreciate Japan culture, Derocque? It is a mistake, for all educated Japan students learn much of English culture and literature. I greatly admire William Shakespeare, and Sir Walter Scott in particular; he indeed sets forth much noble thinking."

"I am not very familiar with them, Sir," I replied, hardly knowing what to say. "Except that I have heard of the English poets."

"Of course, Derocque, you are Frenchman, are you not? I greatly admire the Sir Walter Scott's *Marmion*. I recommend it to you, and when this regrettable war is finished I hope to study it once more. Have you read nothing of *Marmion*?"

"No, Sir," I replied, even as it came to my mind that, in my school days, I had been forced to study it with such good effect that I could remember little or nothing of it.

"It is very interesting story of great nobility, with much teaching for present day," he said, eyeing me intently. "You are not familiar with the story of the Palmer then?"

"No, Sir," I replied with complete truth.

"Ah! Is it not strange that I, an Oriental, should know more of it than you do? Colonel Singh is also familiar with the story, but he will not tell you that. Colonel Singh also says that he thinks that we have your name wrong; he thinks . . ."

He stopped talking for a moment, and at once I became

afraid without knowing why, for Major Tagachaki's face was as bland as ever and his voice as smooth.

"He thinks that it is De Wilton," he went on.

"De Wilton," I echoed stupidly, "De Wilton; who is De Wilton?"

"Well now, Derocque," he said, "I do really believe that you are a very ignorant man; surely you know of De Wilton?"

"No, Sir," I replied with perfect truth.

"I am inclined to believe that you speak the truth, Derocque. Perhaps it is a good thing for you that you do not know De Wilton. I can see, indeed, that you speak the truth. It means nothing to you, does it, Derocque?"

"No, Sir," I replied.

"I believe you, Derocque. If you had known it you must have been very fearful, and there is only stupidity in your face. Many Englishmen would think it clever to play such trick upon Japan soldier."

"Trick? I do not understand."

"Perhaps it would surprise you, Derocque, if I told you that Colonel Singh thinks that you are an Englishman."

"But, Sir," I stammered, now thoroughly terrified, "You know——"

"I do know, Derocque; and it as well for you I do know that you have been vouched for by our Intelligence authorities. I know something of the way that you came here; and Colonel Singh only knows what I have told him. But, apart from that, I know that you are not an Englishman. Do you know how, Derocque?"

"No, Sir," I said, relieved beyond words.

"Very simply. I have penetrating eyes, and I could see that you spoke truth when you said you did not know the story of the Palmer, nor did the name De Wilton mean anything to you. The educated Englishman must know these things, if educated Japan soldier knows them!"

With that he smiled blandly, and left me to my bewildered thoughts. I turned the matter over and over in my mind, but nothing would come clear. For the life of me I could remember nothing of the story of *Marmion*. In the end I had to leave the problem unsolved, for there was, of course, no possibility of looking the story up.

Long afterwards the opportunity did come my way, and I read Scott's masterpiece carefully from end to end; then the mystery was revealed. I still stand amazed when I think of the amazing similarity of my own story and certain aspects of Scott's account of De Wilton disguised as the Palmer in his role of guide to Lord Marmion; in the words of one commentator:

"He is melodramatically effective as the silent Palmer, but the poet concedes him no initiative. His association with Marmion's Train in the journey to Scotland is accidental; the combat at Gifford ends in a fruitless victory for him; and it is only by a most improbable coincidence that he becomes possessed of the means of vindicating his honour."

Major Tagachaki was an intelligent and ruthless man, widely travelled and well educated, and yet he was completely incapable of adequately appreciating the situation so far as I was concerned. He did not realise that an average Englishman of reasonable intelligence and fair education could be so ignorant of one of the classics of his own language and nation; and so careless in general outlook as to have waded through a literary masterpiece without absorbing it. He only knew that, with the ingrained obedience to those in authority that was first and second nature to him, the average Japanese would have absorbed it. So perhaps he failed to see the obvious. Colonel Singh saw it; that seems more than clear to me now, and I still wonder about him, tall, straight, black-bearded, proud and haughty man that he was; and I ponder the motive that had made him turn traitor and exchange one allegiance to an alien rule for another, and, in particular, the constant humiliation that must have been his from being under the command of an officer of rank inferior to his own.

I SHOW THE WAY

THE road from Kalewa to Tamu runs almost due west for the first twenty miles after leaving Kalewa; that is twenty miles measured along the twisting road and not in a direct line and, for the whole of that distance, it follows the valley, or gorge, of the river Myittha running down to join the Chindwin. It is a typical hill road, little more than a track carved out from the steep side of the gorge, twisting and turning, rising and falling, as it follows the tortured contours of some of the most broken country in the world. On the left hand is an almost sheer drop to the bed of the broad stream and, on the right hand, the hills run sharply up, their outline blurred by the mass of heavy jungle covering their precipitous slopes, to be lost, in the rainy season, in low-lying clouds. Occasionally there is a small patch of low ground, deposited by the river at a bend, and across this the track runs on a bund, raised above the marshy ground and the Monsoon floods. In such places, too wet even for the exotic jungle trees and bushes, the elephant grass grows in almost impenetrable masses, with its flat, coarse, razor-edged fronds, shoulder high and higher. On the soggy land from which this rank growth springs, and between the tall, waving fronds, live countless bull frogs, great, grey brutes, silent by day, but breaking forth into a continuous hoarse barking and croaking as darkness falls, a noise which goes on and on without ceasing, for as one stops to draw breath, so does another take up the nerve-racking, never-ending strain.

This tortuous track through the Myittha gorge is one of the two just possible routes from Burma to India, the other being the equally difficult route through the

Hukawng Valley, and it was by these two routes that the pitiful throng of refugees tried to make their escape to India, when the Japanese entered Burma in 1942. It is impossible to appreciate the sufferings they endured without having seen the country through which their path lay. But, as I bumped along with the men of the nation responsible for their sufferings, I was able to visualise what happened; the men, women, and children; British, Indian, Anglo-Indian, and Anglo-Burman, from every walk of life, struggling on foot, sore and starving, with the deadly cholera breaking out amongst them, walking until many of them could walk no more, leaving behind them, as they strove to reach India and safety, their treasured possessions, their homes, their once smart cars, many of which still littered the side of the track, stripped of everything of value by the Japanese; and last of all themselves, now bleached skeletons in the jungle by the roadside. And now the same yellow devils were on the march again, with their spear-heads already across the border within striking distance of the fertile province of Assam. Was the tragic story to be repeated; were these all-devouring locusts to sweep across the broad plains of India, leaving a trail of rapine and destruction in their wake? Were British women to be violated and murdered again, like the nurses in Hong Kong, by these half-civilised brutes?

I took a firm resolve there and then that it would not happen if I could help it; and it seemed to me that I stood a fair chance of preventing it, although it was not going to be easy, for I was not dealing with fools. I had to be a sufficiently good guide to avoid arousing suspicion, and a bad enough one to lead them astray, or better still into the hands of our own troops. I had to remember that there were such things as maps, albeit not very good ones, of the border hills, which they could read as well as I. I realised that I needed all the ingenuity that I could muster, and a further good slice of the amazing good fortune which had enabled me to get away with things thus far.

Such were my thoughts as the trucks lurched onwards with the blazing sun overhead, bouncing and swaying and raising clouds of choking dust from the powdery earth road, through the Myittha gorge to the flatter country beyond, as far as the track junction where the rough road divides, one arm to the left and south alongside the Myittha to Kalemyo, Gangaw, and beyond, the other arm to the right and north-north-east, into the mouth of the Kabaw Valley—The Valley of Death—one of the most malarious spots in the whole world.

Here the hills recede to the right and left, and the ground is relatively flat. The jungle, which is of the densest, extends in a tangled impenetrable mass to the sinister hills lining the valley, with scarcely a break for mile after mile, jungle and still more jungle, and the odd patch of the equally unpleasant elephant grass. It is an evil spot, almost completely uninhabited, and scarcely touched by the taming hand of man, where only one code of law holds undisputed sway—the survival of the fittest in very truth—and it was through this awful place that those poor refugees had tried to make their escape!

The journey is a long one, almost one hundred miles, all of it through the type of country that I have tried to describe; yet it was decided to complete it in one day. We started early in the morning, but it was impossible to average more than ten miles per hour, and it was mid-day before we made the first stop. By that time I was completely shaken up by the constant bumping, and half-choked and blinded by the swirling dust. The feeling of elation occasioned by my successful attempt at arson had passed, and I felt very miserable. The magnitude of the task before me, and the dreadful travelling conditions, combined to send my spirits down to zero, so that it was a thoroughly depressed guide who staggered from the truck, when it halted.

Some sort of a meal was provided, but I could eat none of it; I was too depressed to think of eating, so I sat on one side whilst the others consumed what there was. Had I been somewhat less concerned with my own plight I should have realised that there was very little anyway. Actually it was not until we reached Tamu that I discovered that there had been a very drastic cut in the quantity of rice issued, a serious thing to a rice-eating Army; much more so than a similar cut in the British bread ration, since rice forms the principal part of every meal. My fire-raising efforts were already beginning to bear fruit.

The halt was a brief one, and soon we were in the trucks, grinding forward through the swirling dust once again. The character of the countryside changed very little; the same jungle, the same hills stretching on and on in an unending vista, the same dusty, rutty road, leading ever onward, through dry-bedded *chaung*, water splash, or across an occasional wooden bridge, and for a period running parallel with a considerable stream, the Khampat. Towards the end of the afternoon it began to edge over to the left hand, or north-westerly, side of the valley: we were approaching Tamu.

All day long we had been passing convoys and individual trucks, for even the lightly-equipped Japanese armies required a good deal of supply and maintenance, but as we were approaching Tamu we passed a convoy of a very different kind—a column of Allied prisoners on foot. The majority were Indians: Sikhs, Punjabis, Gharwalis, Madrasis, Mahrattas and so on, but there was a sprinkling of white faces also. They presented a picture of utter dejection, as they stumbled along; already their clothes were caked with the fine dust from the road, which their shuffling feet raised in a dense cloud. Ahead of them lay the hundred mile trek through the Kabaw Valley and, after that, an interminable period of semi-starvation and brutal treatment. I watched the shambling mob go past with the same feeling of horror which came over me when I saw the British prisoners in Rangoon, but I had to restrain my feelings since there was nothing that I could do. So the ragged mob passed out of sight, with hanging heads and dragging feet, on their way to captivity.

Soon after this the trucks rattled over a timber bridge spanning a large dry *chaung*, and climbed out of the Kabaw Valley to Tamu itself.

Like so many places marked on the map of Northern Burma, Tamu was little more than a name, a mere group of huts, before the war had come to that out of the way spot and caused it to spring into a township of bamboo buildings. When I saw it, the Japanese were building many *bashas* to replace those destroyed by the British forces when they fell back; which in their turn were to be destroyed by the Japanese, when they retreated. Small progress had been made in the erection of this accommodation, and great piles of boxes and cases were spread around the area, containing ammunition, fuel, clothing, rations, and numberless other items. Living quarters were non-existent—which made little difference to me since I merely started again from where I left off with the column; but not so with Messrs. Ghosh, Parkash, Das Gupta, and the majority of the other I.N.A. officers. The dismay upon their faces was plain to see, when they discovered that they were expected to sleep on the hard ground without any sort of roof overhead; although I can scarcely imagine what they expected to find in such an out of the way spot. They accepted the situation with very bad grace, complaining bitterly to one another, completely ignoring the well-being of their men; a fact which did not pass unnoticed by the Japanese officers, who, with all their brutality, were efficient enough as officers to realise the importance of these things. From that time onwards the Jap officers began to slight their I.N.A. opposite numbers quite openly at every opportunity, expressing their contempt in words, gestures, and high-handed interference, with the result that the already marked cleavage between the oddly-assorted allies became more pronounced; a development which I viewed with the greatest satisfaction.

My possessions when I was still with my comrades had been scanty; now they were even more so, consisting of nothing more than the clothes I wore, and one thin cotton blanket; apart from equipment, ammunition and the automatic pistol. Everyone was equipped in a similar fashion, apart from the Japanese officers who had a species of waterproof sleeping bag. My preparations for the night were consequently of the briefest, consisting merely of finding a relatively smooth patch of ground, and digging a hollow for my hip bone, before wrapping myself in the flimsy blanket.

The place allotted for the bivouac area had formerly been the site of a British camp, of which nothing remained but the charred shells of *bashas*, but the ground was clear of vegetation and consequently there was no trouble to be expected from leeches and the like. I was scarcely concerned with the hardships entailed in living under such primitive conditions. My mind was too full of the possibilities and potentialities of the coming days. Very soon I should be called upon for advice, if nothing more; although I was inclined to think that it would be little more than advice, since the Japanese, who had found their way so successfully in the hills thus far, could be relied upon to get to the railway if they so desired. After thinking about it for a long time, I decided that they would expect me to do most of my work when we were actually through the hills, by leading them to the garage where they would find the buses, and then conducting part of the Force along the road to the western side of Dimapur.

That night a conference of all the officers was held to discuss the plans for the attempt on the railway. I had expected this to be held later, when we were nearer our objective, but apparently it was necessary to press on with all possible speed, leaving nothing until the last moment. The officers assembled in one of the partly-completed *bashas*; of furniture there was none, save for two large tables placed at one end, and the assembled officers simply squatted on the ground. The hut was lighted by a number of oil lamps, which, throwing a dim smoky glow upon the faces and forms of the assembled Japanese officers, served to accentuate their resemblance to the usual caricature of a Japanese soldier: thick horn spectacles, faces hairless, except for a straggling moustache or goatee beard, wide mouths, and prominent teeth. Their spectacles glinted in the dim light as they turned their heads, giving an impression of eyelessness which was more than vaguely sinister. All of them wore their pointed, floppy hats with the red tin stars at the front, and their long swords hung from their waists.

The I.N.A. officers were seated in a group at the far end of the hut; a sullen, discontented look upon their faces showing that they were not at all pleased with the manner in which the conference was being run. The only I.N.A. officer who was a member of the group of senior officers standing behind the two map-covered tables was Colonel Mohindar Singh. The proceedings were conducted in the Japanese language, of which I understood nothing, and they were almost equally unintelligible to the Indians, most of whom only spoke a little of that language. No attempt whatever was made to translate any of the discussions for their benefit, nor were they consulted in any way, and it was made abundantly clear to them that they were there on sufferance.

Colonel Mohindar Singh was an exception to this rule; he seemed to have a fair grasp of the Japanese language; and furthermore, his opinion was constantly sought by the Japanese officers, and a measure of respect always shown to him. His position was becoming increasingly singular with each passing day. He was forced to cleave more and more to the Japanese by the general uselessness of his own officers, although I feel sure he really detested them. He appeared to be unable to bear the very sight of some of his own officers, Ghosh in particular, for whom he had an almost uncontrollable aversion, and avoided them as much as he could. As for myself, I doubt if we had exchanged a dozen words during the whole of the journey from Rangoon.

The conference had been in progress for almost an hour, and I was wearied with the endless chatter, when I was surprised to hear my assumed name called. I looked up with a start, the never very far away feeling of uneasiness coming over me, and saw that it was Colonel Mohindar Singh who was calling to me. My surprise and fear passed quickly away, and I guessed—and rightly—that I was about to be consulted regarding the route to be taken. Rising to my feet, I made my way towards the map-covered table, feeling quite calm and collected although I knew that the crucial moment had arrived, and my ability to rapidly improvise a solution to whatever problem was presented to me was about to be severely tested. The table was covered with large scale maps, vastly superior to the one which was handed to me in Rangoon, which had been of little assistance to me, and behind it stood Mohindar Singh, Major Tagachaki, and two other Japanese officers I had not previously seen. The Colonel opened the proceedings by saying:

"We have been discussing the route to be followed, and we shall now need your assistance. The position is this: Japanese forces are already occupying Ukhrul; which, as you know, is about thirty miles north-east of Imphal, and forty miles south-east of Kohima. The Kohima area is of course already occupied. We shall go first of all, to Ukhrul, as it appears to be the best jumping-off point. Is this so?"

I made no direct reply to his question for I wanted desperately to get a good look at the map on the table: that might help me to think of something. I paused for a moment, seeking inspiration, as if weighing the matter in my mind—which was of course so—and then said:

"If you will allow me to examine the map, I can point out the route very easily, and then you can decide the best line of approach."

He translated my remarks for the benefit of the Japanese, whilst I watched in a fever of anxiety for fear that I might be denied this, my only chance of concocting a feasible scheme. To my great relief they agreed, and so I was given the opportunity I badly needed. I was confident that my map-reading abilities were as good as theirs, consequently I should be able to pick out a route from the map which I could assert was *the* route; and which, from lack of knowledge greater than my own, they would be unable to gainsay.

I looked at the map on the table, and saw that it was a large-scale reproduction of a British map, printed in English and over-printed in Japanese. I was aware that none of the maps of the hill country were particularly accurate, the difficulties in the way of making an accurate survey being too great. Nevertheless they were sufficiently good to show the general outline of the fantastic hills, to mark the villages, and the principal tracks, as well as the larger streams; and that was sufficient for my purpose.

After all, none of the enemy officers present had ever been in that part of India before. So I did one of the snappiest bits of map-reading that I had ever done, and decided upon *the* route.

Now up to this moment I had no idea of the location of the workships and garage of Suleiman Ismail & Sons, the place where we were supposed to find a fleet of vehicles waiting; it had never been mentioned when I was in Rangoon, and I had not dared to ask. The first thing that I saw when I looked at the map was that a number of crosses had been marked on it. There were two blue pencil crosses on the railway, one on each side of Dimapur, and I jumped to the immediate conclusion that they marked the sites of the proposed rail blocks. Near to one of the blue crosses was a red one, and since both of these crosses were to the east of Dimapur, and that was the side from which we were to come upon the railway, I guessed that the red cross marked the location of the workshop. Furthermore, it was on the outskirts of a small town called Naojan, approximately fifteen miles from Dimapur, where one would expect to find such a garage and workshop. In addition I saw that a large stream, flowing down from the hills, passed near to this place; whilst a track leading from a point on the Manipur Road south of Kohima, and therefore in Japanese hands, crossed the upper reaches of the stream. That was my route. It was the wildest of guesses, of course, and I had no more idea than the Man in the Moon if the route was a possible one.

This rapid thinking had taken but a minute so I was able to explain my choice of route and my reasons for recommending it, without delay.

"To reach Naojan," I said, watching the faces around me to catch any sign of surprise at the mention of that place, "and the buses," and again I paused, but there was still nothing to tell me that I was wrong; so I went on, confident of having surmounted the first obstacle, "it would be better if we followed this route leading from the road near to Kohima, rather than the one leading over the hills from Ukhrul."

I waited whilst this was translated for the non-English speaking Japanese.

"The advantages are that a good part of the journey can be made along the Manipur road itself, now that it is in our hands, enabling quicker progress to be made, and thereby avoiding a good deal of difficult cross-country work. If we start from Ukhrul, the entire journey must be made by rough tracks and paths; the distance is at least seventy miles in a direct line, and such a journey could not be managed in less than seven days: whereas by the other route it is only twenty-five miles or so along the track to the stream—here—and little more than twenty miles down the stream to the railway."

As I stopped speaking I watched them closely whilst the translation was made, hoping that my suggestion of the possibility of a speedy journey would have the desired effect, in view of the growing food shortage which was making itself felt. They chattered together for some minutes, and then addressed a question to me through the medium of Mohindar Singh.

"How much of this route do you know?"

"From Naojan as far as the point where the track crosses the stream."

"What is it like along that stream?"

"Difficult, but possible," I replied. "In any case it is the best way to approach the railway. It is not a usual track, and therefore it will not be guarded. It also provides a covered line of approach almost as far as the railway."

I gave these answers with an air of wholly spurious confidence. They were not to know that my statements were based entirely upon the information supplied by the map—although I flatter myself by thinking that they were sound—too much so, it afterwards appeared. I was gambling upon the existence of a feasible route, or at least one which would not expose me as a hollow fraud, and my experiences with the column had shown me that such routes were possible to a lightly equipped body of men and mules, if they were really determined. My principal reason, however, for putting forward this scheme was that it would be necessary for the Force to go almost as far as Kohima itself before leaving the Manipur Road: British Forces were still in that place, and I might be able to make my escape.

I was asked a few more questions of a similar nature, then a lengthy discussion ensued between the four senior officers. In the end Major Tagachaki made up his mind, decided to follow my suggested route, and announced the change of plan to the other officers who had not been consulted; but no attempt whatever was made to translate this information for the benefit of the I.N.A. officers, who, I could see, were growing more and more discontented.

Seizing the opportunity, I spoke to the I.N.A. Colonel.

"I should like to suggest that the I.N.A. troops take British uniforms with them. They could easily be obtained from some of the prisoners here, and that would enable us to go from Naojan to the other rail block with little risk of detection."

"I have already arranged that," he replied coldly. "Naturally I should not forget such a thing."

I pretended to be crushed by the icy tone of the reply, but inwardly I was rejoicing, for it was exactly what I wanted. The discontent amongst the Indians was growing steadily, and I was sure that I could do a little to foster this state of affairs; whilst the possession of British uniforms was a necessary part of a plan that was beginning to take shape in my mind. I left the hut, after the conference broke up, feeling quite satisfied, and fell in alongside Parkash who was walking away alone. We walked for some minutes in gloomy silence along the muddy path towards our sleeping place beneath the stars, and having made sure of the state of his feelings I proceeded to administer a dose of my poison.

"You don't look very pleased," I said, "what is the matter?"

"No, I am not happy. How could I be with things like this?" he burst out. Then he tried to smooth over what he had said, fearing the consequences of such rash statements. I hastened to reassure him:

"It's all right, I feel as you feel. It is terrible. Why are we slighted in this fashion? All the way from Rangoon they have done nothing but snub us. Why doesn't the C.O. do something about it?"

"I hate him," he replied passionately. "He never acts like one of us; and if I complain about anything he only sneers and tells me to get out. What are things going to be like in India with these Japanese running things? Look at Rangoon: once it was a good place; I know because I lived there before the war, but now nothing is right. Everything is expensive; nothing like cars, and wireless sets can be bought. Everything is breaking down; the roads, trams, railways: everything. We have been promised this, and that, but nothing has come, and I begin to wonder if anything ever will."

"Was Burma a good place before the war then?" I asked.

"Very good. I lived in a good house in Rangoon; there was plenty of food, many shops, cinemas, and very good Races also."

"What was your occupation?"

"I was a clerk in the offices of the Asiatic Trading

Company. Sometimes I wish that I was back there again. Things seemed so different when we were in Rangoon. I didn't think that it would be like this—these terrible hills and jungle. Why, we are even getting short of rice—they say it is because of that fire at Kalewa." He lowered his voice and went on: "Do you really believe what they say about the British running away?"

"No I don't," I said.

"You must know a lot about what things are like in India?"

"Yes I do; and I don't like the sound of some of the things that I hear on the news. You see I do know that many Japanese planes are shot down; yet they never mention that on the wireless. Why, I was in Calcutta when there was a raid, and I saw three Jap planes shot down then."

After this he fell silent; obviously thinking deeply. I said no more; feeling satisfied that I had helped to foster the doubt that was growing in his mind and confident that it would not be very long before he had communicated some of his suspicions to his comrades.

I stretched myself on the ground under the stars that night in an equally thoughtful mood. For a long time I lay on my back looking at the stars shining brightly above me. It was pleasantly cool and a gentle breeze was blowing; the trees on the edge of the jungle were swaying to and fro, and the creak of their branches, and the rustle of the foliage came to my ears as a gentle murmuring sound above the continual harsh chirp of the cicadas. Occasionally, I heard the shrill cry of a night bird or saw the dark outline of a bat as it flitted through the air above me. Once a 'tuk-tu', a species of lizard, filled the air with its croaking cry, four times repeated, then trailing off into silence as if the mechanism actuating it had run down and needed re-winding. Turning my head to one side I could see, bright against the black loom of the jungle wall, thousands of pin-pricks of greenish white light, each one waxing and waning with clockwork-like regularity, visible evidence of the presence of multitudinous fireflies. The sky overhead was like a vast inverted bowl lined with velvet, black and soft; the twinkling stars were glittering gems embedded in its dense blackness, with the icy blue splendour of Sirius like a pale water sapphire, the fiery glow of Betelgeuse a smoky ruby, and the brilliant whiteness of the others like so many scintillating diamonds.

The still beauty of the night was not without its effect upon me. The impact of so much quiet splendour upon my being induced within me a sense of awe. I felt so small, puny, insignificant, helpless, as I wondered what the God above and beyond it all thought of the strivings and strugglings of His foolish creatures. The magnitude of the task before me shrank into insignificance. Even the rights and wrongs of the great struggle in which I played a small part, which was to decide for centuries the manner of life, the way of thinking of millions of men and women, lost its urgency. Did it really matter? Did anything matter? Did not events march towards a predetermined conclusion despite the most strenuous efforts made by individual men and women to the contrary?

In such a mood I fell asleep.

THE EDGE OF IMPHAL PLAIN

THE Force was astir before it was fully light, packing and saddling the mules, and otherwise making ready for the journey. The addition of the mule-leaders, all of them Japanese, had brought the strength up to nearly six hundred men, so there were now three Japanese for every Indian; and, as only half of the Indians could be regarded as soldiers, the odds against me had considerably lengthened. On the other hand I was very pleased to see that every Indian, myself included, was issued with an outfit of captured Indian Army clothing, just as the I.N.A. Commanding Officer had said.

By eight o'clock the mules were loaded: some were carrying rifle and machine gun ammunition, and others boxes of shells for the 75 mm. guns. These guns were divided into three parts, each carried by one mule and as the weight of each gun was 1,200 lb., the load carried by each of these particular mules was not excessive. Other mules were loaded with boxes of explosives, and a little in the way of medical supplies, but none of them carried anything in the way of food; that was an individual issue. This amounted to only five pounds of rice per man, and one small tin containing an emergency ration of compressed dried fish, sufficient for one day only. That was all: no fresh food, nothing tinned or dried, and no beverage of any description.

The meagre scale of rations issued was a subject of much comment, particularly amongst the Indians, whose spirits and general morale descended even lower as a direct result. The most optimistic of calculations showed that the journey could not be done in less than six days, including the time taken to travel from Tamu, through Palel, around the edge of the Imphal Plain, to Kohima. The distance is about one hundred and twenty-five miles in a direct line; and it is quite impossible to travel in anything like a direct line, both in the vertical and the horizontal plane, because of the broken nature of the country. Even the Japanese were disconcerted by so inadequate a quantity of food, which, stretched to the absolute limit, could not last for more than eight or nine days; and, in that time, the Force had to find its way over miles of trackless hills and jungle, establish itself in two defensive positions, and by some means or other find a supply of food sufficient to last until it could link up with the Japanese troops advancing down the Manipur Road.

Major Tagachaki, fully realising the probable effects of such a shortage, was moved to protest to the local commander, but with no result whatever, beyond the offer of a quantity of damaged rice left behind by the retreating XIVth Army. Apparently there was a sudden and quite unexpected shortage of this staple commodity, caused, so it was said, by a recent disastrous fire at Kalewa! Of course, the matter would be rectified in about a week, after fresh supplies had been brought up. The dire necessity was regretted: but there was nothing that could be done about it! This isolated incident threw into sharp relief the risks that were constantly being taken by the Japanese Commanders; the entire Japanese effort was seen to be one in which everything was in the shop window, and nothing on the shelves at the back of the counter—everything in the attack, nothing in the way of reserves.

In the end Major Tagachaki decided to take the damaged rice, several mule loads of it. I wondered at the time what was the matter with it, but I did not find out until much later, when it was to form yet another link in the chain of events which had already led me into so many strange adventures.

I had purposely avoided the jemadar as much as I could during the journey from Monywa, but now I sought him out, drawing him to one side before we moved off.

"Well, Jemadar Sahib," I said, "how are things going now?"

"Very bad, Sahib," he replied with downcast face. "We all begin to feel that we are going to our death. This rice, Sahib; how can a man live on it? Then we have learned that there is no more food coming to us when we leave here."

"That is true," I answered. "This is a suicide attempt; none of these men will live through it. Think! We are going forward over this dreadful country, where nothing grows, with little food; nothing can be brought to us where we are going and, when we get there, we shall be surrounded by British and Indian troops. These Japanese will dig themselves into bunkers, and die like rats in them for the glory of their Emperor. Is that a fitting end for a Sikh, Jemadar Sahib?"

"No Sahib, but what to do? These Japanis will kill us, if we refuse to go."

"I will tell you: you must trust me still more. I do not intend to die with these men, neither need you nor your men. When the time comes I will tell you what to do, and we shall all leave these Japanese. You will be able to get back to your regiment, and you will also be able to go back to your village."

At the mention of his village he burst out:

"My village, Sahib! If only I could. I have one old father and two strong sons that I would see."

"You must go to your men, and tell those that you trust what I have told you. But you must be very careful.

For the time being you must carry on as if nothing has happened, until I tell you what you must do."

With these words I left him, confident that I could count upon his support when the time came.

At about eight-thirty o'clock the Force formed up ready to leave Tamu for Palel. We were to follow the road as far as Palel; and there we should leave the road and take to the jungle to avoid entering the Imphal Plain, still strongly held by the trapped British and Indian troops. It is a journey of something like thirty miles, measured along the twisting road, thirty miles of very stiff going. Once again we should be travelling through the true hill country, the comparative flatness of the Kabaw Valley left behind, and once more surrounded by the fantastic forbidding hills, and the gloomy jungle.

My place was near to the end of the long ragged column, and I could see it stretched out before me along the road, six hundred men and one hundred mules, forming up ready to start. At the head of the Force was a standard bearer carrying a large Rising Sun flag, and around him a group of about forty infantrymen and one officer were drawn up; that was one of the Rifle Company platoons. The entire Force was forming up in 'advance to contact' the usual formation when advancing through thick country towards the enemy. Each unit and sub-unit was easily distinguishable. The Force was little more than a modified Japanese Infantry Regiment, reduced in size and shorn of all administrative personnel; and consisted of Force H.Q., numbering fourteen officers and men, including a small Wireless Telegraphy detachment, two Rifle Companies, one entirely Japanese, the other Indian with a stiffening of Japanese, one modified Gun Company, and a Mule Company.

Each Rifle Company was composed of three platoons and Company H.Q.; the company commander being a

Captain, and the platoon commanders Lieutenants, or Second Lieutenants. The platoons were subdivided into four sections: three of which, each fourteen men in strength, were armed with rifles and one L.M.G. of .256″ calibre, the same as that of the rifle, as the main weapon of each section; the other section was armed with 50 mm. grenade dischargers, a weapon without an exact equivalent in the British Army, smaller even than our 2″ mortar.

The Company H.Q. consisted of one machine gun platoon armed with three "92" medium machine guns of 7.7 mm. calibre, one Mortar Platoon whose armament consisted of three 81 mm. mortars, and a medical detachment.

The Gun Company was organised on similar lines: the armament being the four 75 mm. guns, with rifles as personal weapons. The only arms carried by the Mule Company were the ordinary long-barrelled rifles, which were carried by every man, together with the usual long sword bayonet.

The total armament of the Force may then be summarised as:

75 mm. (2.95″) Mountain Gun	4
81 mm. (3.19″) Mortar	6
50 mm. (1.97″) Grenade Thrower '89' ...	18
6.5 mm. (.256″) Light Machine Gun. 'Nambu'	18
7.5 mm. (.303″) Medium Machine Gun 'Juki'	6
6.5 mm. (.256″) Rifle '32' with bayonet	500 approximately

From this it will be seen that the Force was a formidable fighting organisation—even though the proportion of automatic weapons was smaller than is usual in the British Army, and far smaller than in Wingate's Special Force—and was capable of doing considerable damage; especially if given time to dig in.

The 'advance to contact' formation that I have mentioned was formed by having one Rifle Company in the lead, followed by Force H.Q., next came the Gun Company, and last of all, the mixed I.N.A. and Japanese Company. The Mule Company was of course, spread throughout the column.

All this I could see very easily as it formed up on the winding road with the eternal hills and jungle as the background; and a very sinister and extremely business-like picture it made. The morning sun glinted on the rifle barrels, and on the round, close-fitting steel helmets worn by every man over his pointed cloth cap; whilst an occasional flash of golden light from the mule harness, an offence against good camouflage, revealed a worn and polished spot on the brass fittings and buckles. Generally speaking though, the camouflage was good; the khaki of the uniforms, and the drabness of the leather equipment blending smoothly into the dull green of the foliage. Even the barrels of the mountain guns on the backs of some of the mules were painted a suitable drab colour, and the mules themselves were dark brown or black in colour, with no light spots.

The load carried by each man was comparatively light; being merely a bag of rough canvas slung over his shoulder containing his meagre rations, one tin food bowl, a cotton blanket, and a paper packet containing first aid materials. The contents of the latter are of interest, throwing some light on Japanese medical practice, and were: one small linen-covered packet containing a dressing and a bandage, and a little container of 'Tera-boru' powder, intended to serve the same purpose as our sulpha drugs; that is, to be poured into open wounds.

The time taken to marshal the Force preparatory to moving off was comparatively small, considering the number of men involved; this may be attributed to the good discipline of the troops, and the competence of the junior officers. The mixed Rifle Company was a notable exception. The discipline was fairly good, but patchy, and was rather the discipline of fear than that of willing obedience to authority—and the reason was not far to seek. The I.N.A. officers, almost without exception, were incompetent, mere clerks in khaki and, because of this obvious incompetence, the men had absolutely no confidence in them; lacking as they did, professional ability to temper the brutality with which they, in imitation of the Japanese officers, handled—or mishandled their troops.

The great part of the Force had been ready and waiting for some minutes, but the I.N.A. Company was still in a state of complete confusion. Men were wandering around looking for their platoons whilst the officers shouted confused and contradictory orders. After a while, I saw the squat figure of Major Tagachaki accompanied by the tall I.N.A. commanding officer come striding along the road towards us; and I expected fireworks.

They burst into the confusion like a whirlwind, slapping faces to right and to left, and rapping out sharp orders. Within a few minutes they had reduced chaos to order, and the company began to take shape—with the sole exception of one platoon commanded by the unfortunate Ghosh. This platoon, composed principally of Rangoon Indians with some Sikh and Punjabi N.C.O.s, had all along been remarkable for its inefficiency, even by comparison with the rest of the I.N.A. Company. Ghosh was flapping about in an ineffectual manner at the edge of the meleé, and it was plain for all to see that he had completely lost control of his men: it was also very plain to Colonel Mohindar Singh who watched the performance with a face like thunder. Major Tagachaki fell back, leaving the I.N.A. C.O. to deal with the matter. This he proceeded to do without delay, striding into the crowd, repeating his former tactics with great vigour.

For a while all went well, and the platoon began to take shape; and then the wretched Ghosh who had been gaping at the scene suddenly jumped to life and dashed after Mohindar Singh, slapping faces to right and to left. Then it happened in the twinkling of an eye. Ghosh dealt a vicious blow to one of his havildars, a burly man with a heavy black beard who had been standing quietly by. The man staggered from the blow, delivered with all the malice of a weak nature behind it and then, turning upon his assailant with blazing eyes, dashed his fist into his face, felling him to the ground.

For a long minute there was dead silence. The troops gazing aghast at the paunchy Ghosh, sprawling on the ground with a trickle of blood running from the corner of his mouth, the burly Sikh standing over him, still glaring defiance, and the grim figure of their own C.O. slowly turning on his heel to stare in frozen silence at the scene before him. Then, without another moment's hesitation, Colonel Mohindar Singh whipped out an automatic pistol from the holster at his side—and shot the havildar through the heart.

He dropped like a pole-axed steer, his turbaned head striking the dusty ground with an audible thud; and there he lay, with a dark patch of blood slowly spreading over the front of his tunic. A shocked silence descended upon the Indians as they gazed with incredulous horror upon the dead Sikh. Ghosh, the foolish cause of it all, climbing clumsily to his feet with a look of amazement upon his face, and the Sikh Colonel, stock still save for his watchful eyes, with the pistol still levelled, a faint wisp of blue smoke curling from the long barrel. I am convinced that he regretted his rash action immediately, although he showed no sign of it; instead he slipped the pistol back into the holster, and barked a few sharp words at the gaping Indians.

With ludicrous rapidity they hastened to obey his orders, dragging the dead man to the side of the road, his heels scratching deep furrows in the thick dust; and there he was left for the evil black flies and the scraggy-necked vultures. As soon as this was completed, Mohindar Singh cast another meaning look at the Indians, and then without another word he stalked away, accompanied by Major Tagachaki, and the confusion in Ghosh's platoon sorted itself out as if by magic.

As soon as he was out of earshot, a sullen murmur broke forth from the Indians; an evil sound, charged with hatred, emanating from no particular individual, felt rather than heard. I sensed this feeling running through the entire mixed company, and I knew that this strong undercurrent was running deep and fast, its malevolence directed both against the Japanese and their own C.O., waiting for the opportunity to burst into positive action, restrained only by fear. There was as yet no actual manifestation of this feeling, but it was there for all that, and could be gauged from the evil glances and covert whisperings.

I edged near to Jemadar Gurbaksh Singh to discover his reactions, since he was the man round whom my still nebulous schemes revolved, and if possible to fan the smouldering fires. One look was sufficient; as he looked back at me without speaking I read all that I wanted to know, and I do not think that I have ever seen such an intensity of pent-up fury as I saw then, mirrored in his deep-set eyes.

"Sahib," he finally said, or rather hissed, "You can trust me for anything. I have seen enough in this day's work to know what things will be like if these Japanis get to India. Nand Singh was my friend for many years; now he is dead, shot like a dog by that ——. I swear that before many days are past I will cut his throat—and that Ghosh likewise—that Bengali ——!"

"You are right, Sahib," I replied. "This is murder, and the dead man is of your country, perhaps from a village near to your own. This is but the beginning, and who knows what will follow? But you must wait. There is nothing to be gained by rash action now; there are too many of these Japanese for us here; but in a few days it may not be so. You must try to control the feelings of your men. The Japanese must not suspect anything, or they will never leave us alone with but a few of themselves. Counsel your men, that if they would see their own villages again and avenge what has happened today, they must willingly obey such commands as are given to them—until the right moment arrives. Do you understand, Jemadar Sahib?"

"You speak truly, Sahib; we will but cut our own throats. I will do as you say: but cannot you tell me more, Sahib? How much longer have we to endure their insults?"

"That I cannot tell you; but you must go now, for we must not be seen talking together too much."

With that we parted, and I joined the small group of Japanese and I.N.A. Officers who formed the mixed Company H.Q. As I walked away, I caught several interested glances from some of the Indians—evidently those to whom Jemadar had confided the true facts about myself.

There was no more bother after this incident. Mohindar Singh had made it only too plain by his ruthless action what the consequence of any insubordination would be. He was no fool, and must have been well aware of the hatred of which he was the object, considering no doubt that stern and determined methods were the only ones by which he could hope to handle the motley crew under his command. Had there been no other factors to consider he must have succeeded, for, brave as the Indians could be, they lacked initiative, had there not been a 'nigger in the woodpile' in the shape of myself to fan the smouldering embers, and form the nucleus of a possible defection. My greatest strength lay in the fact that, apart from what Colonel Singh thought, I seemed to be unsuspected; the manner of my arrival in Burma being well known amongst the Force officers and, so long as I took care not to arouse doubts in their minds, I could organise things with little fear of detection, now that I was reasonably sure of the attitude of mind of the Indians.

Ghosh was strutting about like a fat black pouter pigeon; in some way or other he had ascribed to himself a good deal of the credit for his part in the killing of Nand Singh. The submissiveness of his own men, after the salutary example shown them, filled him with such conceit that I confidently expected that he also would draw a pistol on the next man who showed a trace of insubordination. I could scarcely keep the contempt that I felt for the man out of my eyes, when he came up to me in default of another listener, and said:

"That is the way to treat them, eh Derocque? To think that he could knock me down and get away with it! I am only sorry that the C.O. shot him before I had the opportunity. Not that I would have shot him out of hand like that. That was too easy. I should have given it to him in the stomach, and then he would have had something to think about before he died."

I was too full for words to reply to a remark of such weak-minded viciousness. I have no doubt at all that he would have done exactly as he said—if he was quite sure that his own precious skin was not endangered thereby. Seemingly he took my disgusted silence for tacit approval, for he went on:

"Anyway I shall know what to do in future if there is any more nonsense. I was rather surprised by the way the C.O. stood up for me."

Any further conversation was cut off by a series of high-pitched commands from the front of the column, the warning that we were about to move. Soon the movement of the front of the column had communicated itself to the rear, and we were padding along in our soft rubber and canvas boots through the thick dust which lay inches thick on the rough road. The soft slithering of hundreds of those queer *tabi* made a noise quite unlike the clump of British steel-tipped ammunition boots; a noise that was at once suggestive and threatening. Once more I found myself likening their quiet purposeful advance to that of the all-devouring approach of a cloud of locusts—creeping steadily and remorselessly forward, to utterly consume whatever lay in their path; the mythical Yellow Peril become reality.

I could see the head of the long column wriggling around the contours of the wild hills like an immense snake, its outlines blurred by the cloud of choking dust raised by hundreds of pairs of feet and hooves; now disappearing as it wound into a re-entrant, to appear on the far side of a valley, still pressing steadily onwards. The pace never varied, for hour after hour it went on and on, and on. With the lengthening miles there began to grow within me a grudging respect for the marching ability of the Japanese troops. They seemed tireless; evidence of the rigorous training they had received in preparation for this operation; and I realised why the lightly equipped Japanese Army had been able to appear behind the British lines in Malaya, to outflank our troops again and again.

We stopped only twice during the whole of the day, and then only to eat a frugal meal of rice, cooked before we started in the morning. By late afternoon I was feeling extremely tired and footsore; my feet being particularly painful since I had always been used to stout leather boots; whereas the rubber of the soles of the *tabi* was thick enough, but so soft that I could feel the shape of every stone with painful distinctness. The worst thing of all, however, was the chafing between my big and second toes, caused by the partition in the rubber boots, and the ill-fitting socks which were nothing more than a cylinder of coarse cotton material—with no heel—and no partition between the toes to fit the boots! The effect of wearing such a combination may be imagined. The harsh material of the socks was pulled tight between my toes by that wretched partition, and I could feel the skin being rubbed off—a most painful process.

I was not alone in showing signs of distress. The majority of the Rangoon Indians were far worse. They were just not physically capable of such feats of endurance; undersized even compared with the Japanese, who although small were sturdily built. The other Indians stood up to it quite well, being tough well-developed men.

It was the Ledo Road all over again—the gradients were quite as fantastic, the winding of the road just as tortuous, and the hills as wild and steep and jungle clad. As far as the eye could see, it was one unending vista of hill and valley, spur and re-entrant, convex slope and concave slope, and every other conceivable topographical feature. The same magnificent trees grew with incredible profusion, untold millions of them, their massive crowns of foliage blending together to form a continuous green blanket of immense thickness which blurred and rounded the hard outlines of the hills. On one side was dizzy space and, on the other side of the road, the gloomy green wall of the jungle with never a break for mile after mile.

There was a good deal of other traffic on the road, some of it wheeled, but much of it carried on the backs of mules, and even elephants. The trucks were the usual Japanese three-ton vehicles with a sprinkling of Canadian-built Fords and Chevrolets; standard British Army trucks, recently captured from their appearance. I even saw a number of bullock carts trundling forward laden with boxes of ammunition. I also saw four tanks of an unfamiliar pattern; modern-looking vehicles with six large diameter bogie wheels, and an unusual device resembling a handrail round the outside of the turret. They carried one gun of about one and a half inch bore (37 mm. in actual fact) and two machine guns. Just before mid-day a convoy of guns passed us, sixteen of them all told, twelve of them 75 mm. field guns, long, slim-barrelled guns mounted on two thin pneumatic tyred wheels of large diameter; whilst the other four were 105 mm howitzers, rumbling along on large spoked solid-tyred wheels. They were all drawn by tracked tractors. I imagine that it was a complete battery moving forward.

In the opposite direction, that is moving towards Tamu, were occasional groups of walking wounded attended by medical orderlies, wearing Red Cross arm bands and a dark green inverted 'W' on the breast of their tunics, the usual Arm of Service badge of the Japanese Medical Service. I saw no sign of ambulances for the more severely wounded cases, and I wondered if the Japanese were following a policy, not unknown to them in time of stress, of killing off their badly-wounded men.

We reached our destination, a spot not far short of Palel about an hour before darkness fell, having covered a distance of nearly thirty miles; an incredible distance considering the nature of the country. By the time we arrived I was more dead than alive. By some miracle, all of the Rangoon Indians had succeeded in keeping up with the rest of the Force, and I can only think that it was the dreadful example which they had been given earlier which had spurred them on. They were in a shocking state, scarcely able to drag one foot after the other, and I was sure that many of them would not survive the march over the hills.

We were not far short of the edge of the Imphal Plain where the beleaguered British and Indian garrison was holding at bay the Japanese Army, and the muffled rumble of the guns was plainly audible from time to time, rolling and reverberating round the hills like distant thunder. I had no means of knowing what guns they were, and I feared that they might be Japanese; but I know now that they were the famous British 25 pounders, smashing the repeated attempts of the Japanese to descend from the hills into the plain.

Like the camp site at Tamu, the site of our bivouac was that of a completely gutted British camp, and again there was not a vestige of cover, but the ground was dry and free from vegetation and the attendant leeches, and that helped considerably. I was almost too tired to think of eating, but, knowing that I should need every available ounce of energy in the next few days, I ate my portion of boiled salt rice after it was prepared. The stuff was tasteless, lacking meat or vegetables to give it flavour, and of a distinctly unattractive appearance. It had been cooked on a platoon basis, in four gallon petrol tins over a fire of bamboo, and sufficient was prepared to last until the evening meal of the following day, to avoid the necessity for cooking during the journey. Despite the tastelessness, I found that I could eat all there was—and more had it been available. In fact, I felt positively ravenous when I had finished wiping the last fragments from my bowl.

We were too far away from the Imphal Plain for us to be in any danger of a night attack; but despite this the Force went into a position of all-round defence, with the guns and animals in the centre, the light automatics sited, and sentries posted around the perimeter. My preparations for the night followed the usual simple pattern as on the previous night; the hole for my hip bone was scooped, the anti-mosquito veil pulled over my face, and then rolling myself in my blanket, I settled down to sleep.

NEARING THE OBJECTIVE

THE night passed quietly and I slept soundly until I was awakened by the stirring of the whole camp at first light. For half an hour, the whole Force stood to arms in the growing light; until the gloomy murk of the jungle became the perpetual twilight of day, and the mist cleared from the valleys in which it lay like great masses of fluffy cotton-wool. Then we breakfasted on a small portion of the cold soggy rice, its appearance even more unappetising than it had been on the previous evening. I was proving, however, that hunger is the most effective appetiser and I could have eaten three times my portion.

Before we started, I was treated to my first example of the Japanese methods of hygiene as practiced in the Field. At all the camps at which we had so far stayed, latrines of the open pit variety had been provided and fairly well maintained—even at the camp at Tamu. Here there was nothing at all, and no attempt was made to provide even shallow trenches. As a consequence of this neglect, the area was heavily polluted. The camp site showed every sign of being used as a regular staging point. Other troops had (very obviously) stayed there before us, and others would doubtless follow, and yet this elementary precaution was completely neglected. I was surprised to discover this, for I had seen something of the Japanese preoccupation with the prevention of disease in their Base areas whilst I was in Rangoon, where there had been vaccination and inoculation campaigns for the civilian population.

A nearby stream was used for ablution purposes;

which would have been reasonable enough, if the drinking water had not been drawn from the same place, and frequently downstream of the ablution point. At all the more permanent camps, hot water ablutions were provided, and the men took a hot bath daily. But there also their methods contrasted oddly with our own. A large drum of hot water with a wood fire beneath would be used by as many as twenty men in succession without changing the water, so that the last man bathed in a concoction resembling pea soup. I wondered how long it would be before cases of dysentry began to appear amongst us. A form of water filter was an individual issue. This consisted of a perforated bakelite container with a rubber tube attached and filled with impregnated cotton-wool, each filling of wool being sufficient for ten pints of water; but the supplies of cotton-wool were insufficient to deal with all the water, and the filling of impregnated wool was used for much larger quantities, which could not have been efficiently sterilised. There were two Medical Officers with the Force; yet they made no attempt whatever to alter this unsatisfactory state of affairs.

We were on the move again soon after the morning meal was completed—and this time there was no difficulty with the mixed Company. The effects of the previous day's lesson not yet having worn off.

The sleep had done me a lot of good; even the sores between my toes were not quite so painful. This may have been due to the Teraboru powder, some of which I had applied on the previous evening. Consequently, I trudged along with a will, conscious that every mile was bringing me nearer to the chance of making my escape.

We left the road about an hour after starting, near to a camp site which had formerly been occupied by a

British Mechanical Equipment road building unit of the Royal Engineers. Two of their D8 bulldozers still stood at the side of the road with the radiators smashed in; whilst the recently widened road, with fresh cut bank and the pile of earth over the *khud* side, showed that they had been at work right up until the time when they had had to fall back. Our path lay along a fairly well-defined track, and the going, although bad enough, was nothing to be compared with some of the struggles we had had when I was still with the column. I was to discover that the Japanese seldom or never left the jungle tracks and paths, clear evidence that the methods of jungle warfare devised by General Wingate were as far superior to the Japanese methods, as theirs were to the clumsy British tactics of 1942.

For the whole of that day we travelled; along one track after another, up hill and down dale, through stream and dry-bedded *chaung*, on and on and on, at the same never slackening relentless pace. The dust rising thick from the tracks blinded and choked every man in the Force, for these tracks were well-trodden ones, used by military traffic of every description, since the road through the Imphal Plain was still denied to the Japanese by the presence of the XIVth Army. As we stumbled along, with the rivulets of perspiration cutting channels in the caked dust on the faces of every man, the guns would roll and thunder, the continuous sombre muttering speaking eloquently of a bloody battle raging somewhere over the hills. From time to time the eerie muttering would redouble in intensity, and then the Rangoon Indians would exchange frightened glances, as if they expected a shell to burst in their midst at any moment. It was the first time that many of them had heard the noise of battle, and this noise, together with the pangs of hunger and the murder of Nand Singh on the previous day, had brought them to a true realisation of the desperate nature of their position. The effects of the Japanese propaganda which had induced them to join the I.N.A. had worn off, and they were miserable and terrified little men. Nothing frightened them so much, however, as the manner in which the Japanese discussed their chances of survival. Most of the Japanese were quite convinced that they were going to their death, and they discussed it openly with a complete lack of emotion; whilst some of the officers spoke constantly of the glory of dying for the Emperor. One Japanese lieutenant who spoke fairly good English said to me on one occasion:

"Soon we shall be fighting the last fight to avenge our dead, and then we, and they, will march to Kudan (a shrine near to Tokyo dedicated to the War dead) singing a battle song."

I confess that such blind fanaticism frightened me—if in rather a different manner.

As the day drew to a close, the weary, famished Force halted for the night, occupying a prominent hill feature to one side of the track we had been following. Here a more elaborate defensive position than the one of the previous night was sited, in view of the possibility of surprise from patrols of the surrounded garrison which might be active. Since we were in thick jungle country, every man built some sort of a platform as a bed to lift himself clear of the leech-infested ground. Then the usual concoction of rice was prepared, and the Force, with the exception of the sentries, lay down to sleep.

The next day was a repetition of the previous one. Again we travelled all day along jungle tracks, some of them ankle deep in dust, others ankle deep in mud where the luxuriant jungle growth prevented the rays of the hot sun from drying the ground; with the ever-present insect pests changing with the constantly altering conditions—leeches in the wet jungle, and flies buzzing maddeningly around dust-inflamed eyes in the more open places. We struggled on in a welter of sweat, filth, bites and scratches, muscle-racking fatigue, and the gnawing pangs of hunger. In the late afternoon we came out on to the road again having in two days skirted the edge of the Imphal Plain, keeping always in the surrounding foothills, so the distance covered could not have been less than fifty miles. By some miracle or other, all the Indians still managed to keep up, but many of them were in a shocking state, as they stumbled blindly along, driven only by the fear of the consequences of falling out. It was clear that two or three of them were at the end of their tether; their faces grey-green beneath the dark pigment of their skin. Their officers were too much concerned with their own troubles to do anything about it, or, like Mohindar Singh, too ruthless and high-handed to feel sympathy for a weakling, and so, in the end, I drew the attention of one of the Jap Medical Officers to their deplorable condition. He made an effort to do something for them, and later in the day ordered their evacuation to an *Eiseitai* (Divisional Medical Unit) which we happened to pass.

The following day found us moving down the Manipur Road itself and, as a result, travelling conditions were much better. There was very little wheeled traffic—evidently the Japanese had been unable to bring up any of their own vehicles over the rough tracks at their disposal—consequently there was little dust. Furthermore the road was smoothly tarmacked and well-graded and in excellent condition; a real testimony to the skill of the XIVth Army Engineers who had converted it from a bullock-cart track to its present status of a good mountain road, equally as good as the much more widely publicised American-built Ledo Road. Naturally the gradients were still severe, and the hair-pin bends just as frequent, but these features had been reduced to a minimum by careful siting.

The journey to Kohima took nearly two days; the distance is more than fifty miles, and we finally arrived near to that village at about three o'clock on the fifth day after leaving Tamu. Our rations were divided up to last for three more days, and that was all; after that there was nothing but the damaged rice, and no possibility of obtaining more until some could be looted in Assam; yet despite this the Japanese Officers were confident that they would be able to fulfil their mission. The situation was no more desperate than many that they had faced in the past; indeed much of the Japanese success in 1942 was due to this readiness to accept risks, and sail very close to the wind. Nevertheless, there was a noticeable slackening in the speed of the advance; almost unconsciously the leaders had reduced their pace as their reserves of energy diminished, their bodies unequal to the demands made by their fanatical minds. Some of the men were beginning to suffer from diarrhoea, which was probably dysentry in its early stages, and others, myself included, were beginning to show signs of beri-beri. In my own case, the dreadful feeling of weakness, when everything tended to become 'too much trouble' was more marked at the end of each day, and I literally had to force my unwilling body to even prepare a bed for the night. Attempts were made to treat these distressing conditions by administering refined charcoal to the diarrhoea cases, and 'Ebios' (Vitamin B) tablets to the beri-beri cases.

As we approached Kohima, signs of activity became more marked; camps had been set up at the sides of the road—well-concealed beneath the trees, small store dumps established, and the paraphernalia of the Japanese

Signal Corps—signal cables festooning the trees, and wireless aerials—indicated the presence of an important Formation Headquarters. We were passing the forward H.Q. of the Japanese 31st Division which was investing Kohima.

I had been studying a map which had been given to me at Tamu very carefully, and I saw that the track which I had chosen as the beginning of my 'route' led away due north from the road, which turned north-west in the direction of Dimapur. The contour lines told me that I should be able to see Kohima itself from across a broad valley before the hills cut across my line of sight, and I wondered if the time had come for me to make my attempt at getting away.

Everyone had expected that we should camp for the night at the edge of the road and take to the track in the morning; but it was otherwise. I was called to the Force H.Q. and informed that I should stay there until further orders to act as guide. In view of recent developments it was necessary to push on as far as possible that night before halting; I was not informed what they were, but I know now that the Japanese had got wind of the imminent despatch of the British 2nd Division from Ahmednagar in India, and were desperately anxious to prevent their arrival at Dimapur.

I found the track and road junction with very little difficulty; in that type of country there are few places suitable for the construction of roads or tracks, and all those hill roads are remarkable for the way in which they go on for mile upon mile without a single junction; consequently when a well-defined track led off to the right I knew that it must be the one marked on the map. The road had been running downhill for some time, now it entered the mouth of a broadening valley, clinging to the left wall, whilst the track, forking right, maintained its elevation near to the top of the hill forming the right wall. After travelling for about half a mile the whole valley was spread out before me—and I saw Kohima.

It was an unusually broad vista in that country of narrow steep-sided valleys, and the valley must have been at least a mile in width. The course of the road was plainly visible as a narrow band, black against the green of the jungle, winding and turning as it descended through Kohima, and then climbing beyond to disappear round the end of the valley. Kohima itself appeared as nothing more than a mere cluster of buildings, the details indistinguishable at such a distance, nestling in a fold of the hills. A more peaceful scene would be difficult to imagine, for there was neither sight nor sound of the opposing forces, apart from a heap of earth across the road at the spot where it disappeared round the bend in the direction of Dimapur, marking the position of a Japanese road block formed by blasting the steep bank down on to the road. So quiet did everything appear that I wondered, with severe misgivings, if the garrison had been overwhelmed; but the sight of the road block still across the road served to reassure me.

I looked and looked, but still I could see nothing. The road was deserted, and the green blanket of the jungle hid everything else from my eyes; yet beneath that blanket the desperate Indian and British garrison was still holding at bay the crack Japanese 31st Division. I have learned since that, by the time I arrived in that area, the struggle had gone on for days with scarcely a break, and the blackened fly-infested corpses lay where they had fallen to stink and rot in the humid sub-tropical heat, neither side daring to emerge into the open to retrieve their dead. The scratch garrison was hanging on tooth and nail in a hell of stench, thirst, hunger, and nervous tension, with ammunition running short, and no sign of the longed-for relief.

On the following morning, we were on the move again at a very early hour, pushing forward at a rapid rate. I learned that a message of some sort had been received by wireless; and from the pace set by the leaders, I guessed that it stressed the need for the utmost speed. All day long we travelled, on and on, never slackening for an instant, struggling and scrambling along the narrow track. Sometimes we were following a tunnel-like path with the jungle all round and overhead, or pushing along the bottom of a narrow valley over the smooth stones of the torrent bed, and on other occasions the track climbed dizzily up the side of one of the innumerable steep-sided hills, round and round, up and up, with nothing but empty space and a drop of several hundreds of feet to the valley below. At times the column straggled, then the Japanese officers would shout and slap the faces of the laggards until they succeeded in closing up. Men and animals were pressed to the limit—and beyond it—dysentry had begun to make its presence felt, attacking both Japanese and Indian with complete impartiality, and reducing its victims to a state of complete weakness and near exhaustion.

I was travelling with the Force H.Q. so I had little opportunity of seeing how the Indians were faring at the rear, but from what I saw of the Japanese I guessed that they must be making heavy weather of it. Many of the Japanese were hanging on to some part of the mules' harness for support and assistance in the bad places, their usual chattering silenced, their bland faces, usually expressionless to my eyes, showing definite signs of great distress. My own weakness had increased somewhat, although I was still free from dysentry, and I also had to lean heavily upon the support offered by one of the sturdy mules. I was constantly ravaged by the pangs of hunger; although some of the dysentry sufferers had lost the desire to eat, a symptom of the brand of the disease from which they were suffering.

When the usual brief halt was made for a scanty meal, the men collapsed, panting for breath and streaming with perspiration, and it was only with the greatest difficulty that they were slapped and kicked to their feet. Yet despite this brutal treatment, the Jap soldiers endured their sufferings stoically, responding mechanically to the constant goading, literally flogging themselves to keep moving.

Despite my own sufferings which were not inconsiderable, I was able to marvel at the dumb discipline of the Japanese troops; treated like dogs by officers who treated themselves in the same manner, they were enduring incredible hardships, yet at the end of this gruelling journey they would be ordered to dig defensive positions, which they would hold until their nerveless hands could no longer grasp a rifle, or a heavy bullet sped them on their way to the warriors' Heaven. Separated by miles of hill and jungle country from the rest of the Japanese forces, with limited ammunition and no certain supplies of food, they would cling like leeches to the vital railway artery, ravaged by disease, their dead and wounded rotting with the scarcely-living in the stinking foxholes and bunkers, bombed, mortared, shelled, yet clinging fanatically to every inch of ground with no thought of surrender. Not until the last man had been killed, or, their ammunition exhausted, they had blown themselves to the presence of the Sun God with a grenade clasped to their chests, would the positions be over-run.

As I marvelled, so did my anxiety grow. Every mile was bringing this crowd of narrow-eyed fanatics nearer to their objective, and I was powerless to stop them. I dare not leave the Force and try to make my own way to the railway. My rapidly deteriorating physical condition would prevent me from ever completing the journey, and I began to think that the only thing that I could do was to travel with them as far as the railway, and then slip away to raise the alarm, before they had time to consolidate their positions. I had abandoned the wild ideas that I had entertained of leading them away from the railway instead of towards it, knowing full well that if I was as good at map reading as they were, then the reverse was also true. In any case their compasses would soon tell them what was happening if I attempted to lead them in some direction other than north. Whatever happened, I must not lose the confidence that I enjoyed amongst them, for if I by some wild act discredited myself in their eyes I should lose all chances of misleading them when they attempted to find the garage of Suleiman Ismail and their transport.

When we finally halted for the night, it was discovered that twenty of the Indians were missing, two of them officers; one a man named Buksh, and the other that budding great man, Ghosh. Buksh and twelve of the Indian soldiers straggled in one at a time before darkness fell, but the others were never seen again. They must have dropped out too far back to catch up again and, in the darkness, had wandered from the track, becoming hopelessly lost in the jungle. Or perhaps they had stumbled over the precipitous edge of the path to be smashed to a jelly on the smooth water-worn rocks of the *chaung* bed far below. Whatever the reason it was the end of the military career of the former petty official, Captain Ghosh, I.N.A.

The defensive position for the night was prepared with the usual care, in spite of the exhausted condition of the troops, and the unfortunate sentries had to spend part of the night on guard instead of resting their tired bodies. The night passed quietly; showing that the British were completely unaware of the presence of a Japanese force so close to the vital railway.

In the morning when the time came to move, three of the dysentry cases were too weak to walk: two Indians and one Japanese. No attempt was made to fix them on to the back of one of the mules as was the custom in Special Force. Instead the unfortunate men were simply left behind on their rough beds. One of the medical officers lingered behind with two of his orderlies, for the purpose, I supposed at first, of making the doomed men as comfortable as possible; but it was not so, and three sharp cracks told a very different story. As the sound of the pistol shots came to my ears, I was unable to repress a feeling of horror. War is a horrible and brutal business, and this Far Eastern struggle where quarter was scarcely asked or given particularly so; yet this slaughter of their own sick by the Japanese, lest they be succoured by the enemy and induced to give information, possessed a peculiarly evil quality sufficient to strike fear into the heart of the bravest. I scanned the faces of the Japanese for any traces of emotion; but there was nothing. Their bland haggard features were as expressionless as ever, and I shuddered again as I realised that these deluded fanatics, this unholy product of Western material progress and Eastern tradition, these all-devouring locusts, were drawing nearer, ever nearer to the broad plains of India.

That day was a repetition of the previous one; forward at the same mad pace, over, around, and through all obstacles, stream and bamboo thicket, rugged rocks and glutinous swamp: torn, scratched, bitten, bleeding, soaked with perspiration, ravenous with hunger, shattered by disease; on and on and on till everything was blurred by a red mist of pain and misery and every step forward a mighty effort. At mid-day we stopped for a prolonged rest to allow the stragglers to overtake the Force, to enable the exhausted men to recover, and also because we had reached the spot where the track crossed the stream, along the course of which I had so rashly stated that it was possible to reach the railway near to Naojan. The track we had followed had led us down from the hills into a valley through which the stream flowed, and then continued away to the north-east. The valley was narrow and filled with dense jungle and, of course, there was no sign of a path leading along it. A discouraging outlook so far as my personal safety was concerned.

Before I had time to ponder this, I was called before Major Tagachaki and Colonel Mohindar Singh, and informed that I was now expected to lead the way down to the railway. Realising that any sign of weakness on my part would be fatal, I jumped headlong into another of my wild fabrications, feeling uneasily that I was getting near to the end of my tether. I knew only one thing—the stream must eventually flow down into the plain, and if water could get there it was at least possible that men also could; although that by no means followed. Anyway I had to say something. So it was with an air of confidence, wholely spurious, that I informed them that the way for the most part lay along the bed of the stream.

As I made this announcement the two enemy commanders looked at me very searchingly — almost suspiciously I felt—and I was horribly afraid. Yet they said nothing beyond asking me if I was quite sure of the way: to which I replied in the affirmative, saying that they "would soon see": what I knew not!

I took my place with the leading platoon and led the way along the rocky bed of the stream. I doubt if the water was more than two feet deep at the deepest part, although in the Monsoon season it would be a raging torrent, but rapid progress was quite impossible, for the few inches of water at the edge of the stream would suddenly deepen to a foot or eighteen inches, and the water prevented rapid movement of the legs. The stream itself was about twenty feet in width, not more, flowing between high banks bearing many marks of the flood which poured between them during the rains. The jungle grew right down to the very edges of the banks on each side, arching out towards the middle of the stream, and in many places meeting to form a solid green vaulted roof overhead almost as dense as the foliage at the sides, but in other places scanty, affording a glimpse of the blue sky above. Here and there a huge tree lay across the stream like a suspension bridge, the trunk forming the roadway and the festooning creepers the suspension cables. Of life there was little sign, apart from the occasional bird which fluttered away at our approach, and no sound disturbed the stillness but the clatter of the mules' hooves on the rocks, the jingle of harness, and the occasional chatter of the Japanese soldiers. A strange place indeed; perhaps never before trodden by the foot of man.

For several miles it was the same, and then the banks of the stream began to get higher and the light to fade until it was no more than quarter light. I was filled with mingled hopes and fears: perhaps the route was impossible after all; but if it was, what was to be the fate of the unfortunate guide?

So we continued. My doubts grew stronger as the vegetation began to thin out and great slabs of bare rock appeared, and the banks of the stream grew higher and higher. Soon we were in a narrow gorge, the sides rocky and bare, a narrow strip of blue sky overhead, and the stream flowing narrower and deeper, first of all knee deep, then thigh deep, with the current growing stronger and stronger.

The doubts that struck me also struck the Japanese, for a message came up to me from Mohindar Singh asking me if everything was all right. I replied in the affirmative!

After a while, it was difficult to keep a footing on the smooth rocky bed, and I had visions of being swept forward into the very bowels of the Earth, which was where the stream seemed to be flowing; but still I went forward—there seemed to be nothing else to do! Despite the absence of vegetation, it was still very dim at the bottom of the gorge, and I could see little beyond the smooth grey walls of rock on either side, and the smooth black surface of the water. I was none too sure of the time, but I knew that the afternoon must be well advanced, and the idea of spending the night in such an eerie place did not appeal to me at all, consequently I proceeded as rapidly as I dared.

Eventually the light began to grow stronger, and an elongated vee of brightness appeared ahead. At the same time the rocky bed of the stream began to slope downwards, and the force of the water rushing past increased accordingly. Several times I almost lost my footing but managed to recover myself, and then, just as I thought that the current was easing slightly, my feet went from under me, I shot full length into the stream—and away.

Before I realised what was happening, I had swallowed a generous mouthful of water, received a couple of violent bumps on the rocks, and then found myself floundering in a wide shallow pool in broad daylight. I scrambled to my feet, found that the water did not exceed three feet in depth, and then I looked around me and saw where I was.

THE PHALLIC SYMBOLS

I WAS at the base of an enormous cliff-like hill, which towered hundreds of feet above me, wrapped in the usual blanket of green jungle. Right down the centre of this massive wall was a tremendous vee-shaped rent, remarkable for its height and extreme narrowness; and from the bottom of this colossal fissure the stream issued, pouring into the pool in which I stood in a low smooth cascade. The pool was about twenty yards in diameter, and of a smooth and regular outline, evidently owing its existence to the scouring action of the silt-laden water of numberless Monsoon floods. The overflow was at one side, and the out-flowing stream turning at right angles to the line of its former course ran along the base of the hill and disappeared.

Turning away from the hill, still standing in the pool, since to wade out of it would cost me a tremendous effort, I saw that the ground sloped upwards with increasing steepness on the other three sides to a skyline; save in the direction of the flow of the stream where there was a narrow gap. In other words, I was in a bowl scooped out from the side of the hill in the dim and distant past, probably by the action of a much larger stream than the one which at present issued from the gorge. A remarkable feature of the place was the scantiness of the vegetation, except towards the top edge of the bowl where the jungle grew thick. This was particularly so towards the bottom of the bowl, near to the pool, where there was little vegetation apart from a few tufts of coarse grass, and a few straggling bushes growing from cracks in the bare rock from which all soil had been washed; again by the action of the stream when in flood.

The diameter of this bowl could not have exceeded a quarter of a mile, probably less, whilst the depth was somewhere round about one hundred and fifty feet.

Then, as I looked around again, I became aware of some objects of such an extraordinary nature that my interest was aroused. At first I could not imagine what they were, but as I waded out of the water, I saw that they were of stone, and obviously the work of man.

Leaving these extraordinary objects for later investigation, I turned towards the fissure to see if any of the Japanese would emerge therefrom in the same manner as I had done. There was no sign of them. I expect that they halted after I had so suddenly disappeared, wondering where I had gone and not knowing what to do. I made no attempt to shout to them. I was quite sick of their company and I hoped fervently that they would turn back and lose themselves. I was quite prepared to take my chance on my own by this time. Maybe, with a bit of luck, I might reach the railway before they did and raise the alarm. I listened very carefully but I could hear nothing but the noise of the falling water.

So I looked about me to find a place to spend the night, for the sun was declining and I was just about all in. The strange objects which I had seen a little earlier attracted my attention, and I walked over to examine them more closely and discover if they would offer me shelter. Despite my exhausted condition, there was something about them which riveted my attention, although at first I was not aware what it was. I counted five rows of them, with perhaps twenty in a row spaced at regular intervals. They were of varying height, the largest being at least thirty feet high, although the majority were somewhere about half as large. The second and fourth rows were of a different design from the others, being little more than roughly-squared blocks of stone with a deep groove chiselled down the centre. The others were cylindrical, the diameter being about one-quarter that of the height, with a projecting ornamented band running right round the object at a little distance from the rounded, elongated top.

I gazed at these unusual objects for some minutes with my tired brain struggling to comprehend their true nature—even going so far as to lay my hand upon the weathered moss-covered surface to convince myself that they were real. Then I realised what they were. I had heard of the famous 'Penis Park' as it was commonly called, at Dimapur, and I afterwards saw it there, at a little later date when I stayed at No. 3 Rest Camp which was sited around that remarkable Ancient Monument—and this was another such place. These bizarre objects were nothing more than conventionalised representations of human reproductive organs, male and female, symbols of phallic worship.

I was brought back to earth by the sudden realisation that I was not alone. The faintest of movements behind me caused me to turn my head—and I saw something which turned my blood to water. The solemn atmosphere of the place had already had some effect upon me, a feeling commonly induced by some token of a dead and forgotten civilisation; consequently when I saw, not twenty yards from me, a nightmarish figure brandishing a long spear I thought that it was the Devil himself. I gazed spellbound, rooted to the spot, as he advanced slowly towards me, the spear held above his head ready to strike.

All power of movement had gone from my legs, and I could only gaze, utterly terrified by what I saw. It was the figure of a man, naked except for a square of cloth hanging from a red cord tied around his waist, and with a bunch of long hair hanging from the same cord over one hip. Round his neck were two rows of enormous red beads, and his face and chest were painted with horizontal bars of red paint. His hair was fuzzed into a spiked halo, thick with heavy grease, and he was wearing some sort of a feather head-dress. Most frightening of all was the sight of a large bone, pointed at both ends, thrust through the fleshy part of his nostrils, and a pair of similar bones thrust through the lobes of his ears. All these details impressed themselves upon my mind, which was quite clear, in the space of two or three seconds.

Who, or what it was I had no idea. Still he came nearer, and still I was unable either to take to my heels or make a movement towards the automatic pistol in the holster at my side. Then he stopped—and for one long minute looked at me. As he gazed his face broke into a broad grin disclosing two rows of discoloured teeth; then without a word he lowered his spear, and turning away from me padded swiftly between the stone erections to disappear into the bushes. That was the last I saw of him.

As he moved away, the power of movement returned to my legs, and I did as he did—in the opposite direction and as quickly as I could. In a few minutes I became calmer, although I was still afraid and almost wished that the Japanese would appear. I realised, however, that it was not the Devil, but a man of flesh and blood like myself, but I could not imagine what he was. As for spending the night in that place alone with such a wild creature wandering about—the very idea sent cold shivers down my back. For a long time I wondered what he was; but I never knew until several weeks had elapsed when I saw a number of similar wild figures.

In actual fact he was a Naga, one of the savage head hunters who inhabit the border hills, and who proved to be extremely loyal to us during that period when so many people thought that the last days of the British Empire had come, acting as scouts and guides, and killing the occasional Japanese to add to their stock of heads. Without a doubt I had been marked down by that particular Naga as a very desirable specimen; and, had I not turned round when I did, I am convinced that I should have suffered that fate, and my head now be adorning the wall of a Naga hut somewhere on the border between Burma and Assam. As it was, he saw that I was not a Japanese, despite my uniform, and refrained from killing me accordingly; although why he slipped off and left me to my own devices as he did I can still not understand.

I was standing by the pool still thinking about this strange apparition when there was a loud splash, and the figure of one of the Japanese soldiers was struggling in the middle of the pool; apparently having emerged from the fissure in the same manner as myself. He climbed to his feet, and seeing me came splashing in my direction, gabbling something in Japanese and pointing to the waterfall. He had a rope tied round his waist and this he proceeded to tug, evidently as a signal to the still invisible Japs in the gorge. He had apparently been pushed into the unknown by way of an experiment. Almost immediately another Jap shot out, then another, and another, one at a time until the pool was filled with floundering men and mules. Still they came, until the whole Force was standing in and around the basin, the less exhausted men gazing in amazement at the phallic symbols.

I can scarcely say whether I was glad or sorry at the appearance of the Japs. My feelings were mixed, as they had been on so many occasions during the previous weeks. I had devoutly hoped that I would not see them again, but the appearance of the Naga had filled me with misgivings of a personal nature.

By this time the sun was setting, and so preparations were made to spend the night in the basin. I was called to the Force H.Q. expecting to find myself in disgrace—if nothing more—as a result of my disappearance, but to my surprise the Jap officers were grinning broadly, and even Mohindar Singh's grim face was relaxed. It was he, as usual, who acted as spokesman.

"Captain Derocque. You have done well, and for that you will be rewarded. I must say though that we thought that something had gone wrong when we heard that you had been carried away. It is amazing that you should have known of the existence of such a direct route through the hills; and a completely unguarded one at that. It is a good omen, and now we know that we are going to succeed in our mission."

Then it dawned upon me what he was driving at. I became aware of something which I had overlooked before—there was nothing but the darkening blue sky to be seen above the rim of the bowl. The hill at the back towered hundreds of feet above us, and, if there had been any hills of a similar size ahead, they would have appeared above the rim of the shallow bowl. In other words we were through the hills: there was nothing beyond that rim but the foothills descending to the plain below; nothing that would be anything of an obstacle to these determined fanatics. The railway, the vital objective, could not be more than five or six miles away; and was very probably visible from the edge of the basin.

My depression increased.

I AM EXPOSED

IT was the 22nd day of March when the mixed Japanese-I.N.A. Force left the basin of the phallic symbols, two days after the Japanese controlled radio had very prematurely announced the capture of Imphal to the listening world. This 'news' was announced to the entire Force in Japanese and Hindustani just before we started, by way of a stimulus. The general effect of this completely false announcement was smaller than might have been expected; the Japanese accepted it with little sign of enthusiasm, and the Indians were completely apathetic: it seemed as if they were quite overcome by the all-prevailing stench of paraffin, which was still too strong for them. As for myself, I received the story with a growing determination to do what I could to foil this particular part of the Japanese scheme. I was depressed by such a piece of information, which, if true, must be regarded as the worst reverse we had so far suffered in a campaign which had opened so disastrously for us, but even so I was not without a gleam of hope, in strange contrast to my overwhelming depression of the previous night.

The day passed uneventfully as we pushed steadily onwards, and by the mid-day halt the greater part of the journey had been accomplished. Nothing had been seen of any living creature, and it was confidently assumed that the element of surprise was complete. After the usual meagre portion of cold boiled rice had been consumed, no attempt being made to eat any of the contaminated stuff, the Force rested. A reconnaissance party was sent forward to select the best defensive position, and the best line of approach. Within an hour they returned, so close to the railway were we, and after a little consultation between the Jap officers we moved in their wake.

As we moved I caught a glimpse of the surrounding country through a gap in the trees. We were descending the slope of a hill which ran parallel with the railway, still about a mile ahead. Below us, running at right angles to the former hill, was a thickly-wooded saddle connecting the hill on which we stood with a prominent isolated hill, round the end of which the railway curved.

It was one of the long finger-like projections which I had seen from above in the morning, and an obvious place for a defensive position. This particular one had been selected because it extended further into the plain than the adjoining hills, and the saddle connecting it to the hills at the rear was considerably lower than the hill itself, with the surrounding cultivated land broad and open. These features imposed upon any attacking force the necessity of advancing across open country on three sides of the defensive hill, with little cover against the fire of the defenders: or if they attempted to approach from the rear, of negotiating the narrow saddle and still having rising ground ahead of them before they reached the actual Japanese positions. A further advantage was the close proximity of the railway, and a fairly considerable stream running along one side of the hill which would act as an obstacle and afford an ample water supply. No difficulty would be experienced in completely closing the railway, which would be under the fire of almost all weapons at short range.

One disadvantage did exist: the isolated character of the hill and its prominent shape made it a good artillery target; but that is a risk the Japanese were always ready to accept, relying upon the strength of their formidable bunkers for protection. They had a little artillery of their own in the shape of the four mountain guns, which could be used against attacking infantry, in an anti-tank role, and to a limited extent for counter battery work.

My first impressions of the strength of the position were confirmed as we struggled along the saddle, and up the steeply sloping sides of the hill. The hill was elongated rather than rounded as I had first thought, and its sides, clothed with dense jungle, predominately great clumps of bamboo, were of the steepest. These great clumps of bamboo, formidable obstacles in themselves, would provide ample material for the manufacture of *panjis*, those fire-hardened pointed stakes of bamboo, which set in the ground at an angle, formed an obstacle as efficient as any barbed wire fence. A wound resulting from impalement upon their needle-like points was almost certain to become septic.

As soon as the Force was in occupation of the hill immediate steps were taken to put it into a state of defence. The various company and platoon areas were allotted, and all weapons sited. This was done with great rapidity and skill, and in a short time a complete defensive plan was drawn up and the troops were digging in. They used a two-piece entrenching tool for this purpose, which also acted as an observation shield when necessary, two holes bored in the blade enabling the observer to survey the countryside with relative safety. I took the greatest interest in the siting of every position, noting its location, method of construction, and the weapons it contained: information which would materially assist in the reduction of the position if only I could pass it to the right quarter.

The position on the hill was designed for a garrison of one and a half companies, temporarily augmented by the other one and a half companies who were intended to proceed to the other side of Dimapur and establish the other rail block as soon as possible. Great care was taken to avoid revealing the presence of the Force, a matter rendered relatively simple by the density of the jungle. The need for surprise would not be past until the second half of the Force had reached its destination. The defence system was based on a few bunkers connected to a large number of one-man posts without head cover designed for riflemen, connected together and to the bunkers by a system of crawl trenches. Alternative positions for all machine guns were provided, together with sites for the mortars and grenade dischargers. The guns, of which two were being assembled, were to be provided with log emplacements, so sited that they could cover the railway as well as the surrounding country. It would take several days to complete the position, but already it would be a difficult matter to dislodge the Japs from the hill—unless!

My grudging respect for the Jap as a fighting man increased, as I viewed these preparations. Despite the hardships they had endured, the disease from which they were suffering, the discipline of the individual soldier was still as good as ever, and they were digging like moles to strengthen the fortress. The Indians were a very different matter: badly led and hardly treated, and held in check only by fear of the consequence of any breach of discipline.

I was banking on what was going to happen when the attempt was made to cook and eat the contaminated rice, which must happen that evening since all the other rice had gone, leaving only the tinned *bonito*—the emergency ration. There was, of course, ample food for the garrison which was to stay in the shape of the mules, now they were no longer needed for transport purposes; but mules, live or dead, could not be taken with that part of the Force to which the more important task of preventing the arrival of the British reinforcements at Dimapur had been allotted. Therefore, I argued to myself, an attempt will have to be made to obtain fresh supplies of rice *before* any action is taken against the railway.

So with great impatience I awaited the commencement of the cooking operations.

At last they began; I stood by the tin containers in which the rice was boiling, with the stench of paraffin oil like unto the fragrance of ambrosia in my nostrils. Attempts were made to skim off the oily scum, but with little success. I left the scene of the cooking operations in search of the jemadar, confident of the outcome. I had not the slightest intention of trying to eat the stuff—there was sufficient in the tin of *bonito* to last for the remainder of my sojourn on the hill.

I found him gloomily supervising the construction of a bunker, and drew him to one side.

"Tonight, Sahib," I said, and a look of profound relief flashed into his eyes, his despondent manner dropping from him like a cloak.

"Now listen very carefully," I went on. "Everything depends upon what we do now. Have you a really good, trustworthy man?"

"There is one very good man, Sahib: Havildar Baquat Ali."

"Which man is that?"

"He is one big man with moustache. He is one Punjabi Mussulman; but a very good man and I trust him. He will do anything you say, Sahib."

"That is good. Now tonight a party will have to leave here to get food. This rice cannot be eaten, and you must tell your men not to try to eat it or they will make themselves very sick. They all have a tin of fish;

let them eat that. It is almost certain that your men will go, and you with them, for the Japanese will not show themselves yet. I shall try to come with you, but if I do not come you must just get away and raise the alarm. If I do come, I will tell you what to do."

"After we have gone, Havildar Baquat Ali must stampede the mules. This is very important. He can get a few good men to help him. The best way to do it is to cut them loose, and then throw a grenade into the middle of them. If there is a Japanese guard on the mules they must be killed—silently. After he has done this, he will be able to escape through the part of the defences occupied by your company. By that time all of your men must have gone. Tell them to slip away as silently as they can. Every man who escapes must go as far away as he can from here, and I will see that they are well treated by the British Sahibs, and that they are not punished in any way. Tell all this only to the men who you can really trust, the others must take their chance. Do you understand, Jemadar Sahib?"

"Ji, Sahib," he replied. "It shall be as you say. There is nought but certain death for us here."

With that I left him, returning to where the rice was cooking.

It happened exactly as I expected. The starving Japanese tried to eat the stinking rice, but few succeeded in holding down more than a few mouthfuls, and most of these were violently sick as a result. In the end the attempt was given up, and their C.O. grudgingly gave them permission to open their emergency rations. Soon afterwards I was called before the two C.O.s.

"It is necessary to obtain more rice for our troops to eat," said Mohindar Singh. "This rice cannot be eaten. We think that Suleiman Ismail will be able to supply some without attracting attention, and so we shall be going there tonight as soon as it is dark. To avoid detection a party of my men will go wearing the British uniforms. Captain Dus Gupta will take one of his Sections, and you will go to show us the way, and because you know Suleiman Ismail. I also shall go, so that I can fix up the details regarding the transport as well—and see that nothing goes wrong."

As he made this last remark he shot a quick glance at me, and I was sure that there was a tinge of suspicion in his scrutiny. Perhaps I had been seen talking to the jemadar on several occasions. Yet there was nothing definite to indicate the slightest grounds for suspicion against me. Had I not led them through the hills? Anyway he said nothing which revealed his true thoughts, and very soon dismissed me.

My first action was to seek out Das Gupta and suggest to him that he took the jemadar along with his Section, pointing out that he had real control over the men which might be needed if things went wrong. To my delight he played right into my hands, accepting my advice without question, only too glad to be able to thrust the responsibility for the necessary preparations upon the jemadar's broad shoulders.

We started away about an hour later, dressed in British jungle green; and the very feel of the cloth upon my body seemed to infuse me with a new confidence, banishing the fatigue from my sorely tried body. I felt my old self again; and it was as if I put off the mythical personality of Maurice Derocque, renegade and traitor, with the Japanese uniform. I wore the badges of rank of a Lieutenant—quite rightly so—whilst Mohindar Singh and Das Gupta wore the insignia of a Major and Captain respectively. The sepoys were armed with Japanese rifles, but the difference would not be noticed in the darkness, and they were in all other respects dressed exactly like soldiers of the Indian Army. The officers, including the jemadar, carried pistols. The party numbered seventeen all told, and presented so normal an appearance to the casual observer that it was intended to enter Naojan quite openly and go straight to the garage where we should find Suleiman Ismail.

Crossing the railway, as yet undamaged in any way, we picked our way through the paddy fields in the direction of the road which was just about two miles away. On reaching the road we climbed the bunded sides, and turned right in the direction of Naojan village. After another half an hour the lights of a fairly considerable village loomed up in the distance, and I knew that we were approaching Naojan. I had not the slightest idea of the whereabouts of the garage we were looking for, although I pretended to be perfectly familiar with its whereabouts. I guessed that it would be on the outskirts of the village, such places usually were, and that there would be a prominent signboard advertising the business carried on by Suleiman Ismail & Sons. In any case I should not be over-concerned if I failed to find the place. I was away from the Japanese, and I knew what the jemadar would do if I gave the word.

As a matter of fact, it was not easy to find and, although I kept a careful look out, we passed right through the village without having seen anything remotely resembling a garage. I had a good deal of difficulty in explaining this away to Mohindar Singh; but I told a fairly convincing story of only having been to Naojan once, and that was in the daylight when things looked very different. In the end he lost patience and enquired the way of a passing coolie, who directed us to a lane running from the road. There we found the garage, a large corrugated iron building with an ornate noticeboard outside.

Leaving the rest of us at the gate, Mohindar Singh

walked up to the garage in search of Suleiman Ismail. As soon as he was out of earshot the jemadar sidled up to me, and gave me an enquiring glance: I shook my head and merely said: "Wait." Not that I was at all clear in my mind regarding the plan of action which I was going to follow. That depended upon the trend of events and, besides that, I wanted to find out as much as I could before I precipitated matters.

I could see the Colonel walking round the outside of the garage, looking in at the windows and trying the doors; but the place seemed to be deserted. Eventually he walked over to a house standing at the side of the garage and disappeared from sight. After about ten minutes he re-appeared accompanied by the figure of a civilian, and both of them entered the garage by a side door.

Another five minutes elapsed, and then the Colonel appeared at the door beckoning us towards him. The whole Section walked up the path and entered the building, leaving one man at the door to act as guard. The place was dimly lighted by a single naked electric lamp suspended from the roof, which provided just sufficient illumination to enable me to see the extent of the building, and the nature of its contents. It was long and low, with a concrete floor and a pair of large doors at one end, and a row of twelve decrepit vehicles parked along one side. The majority of them were buses, the usual three-ton chassis of American origin to be seen in India, fitted with locally made bodies of ornate design in apparent danger of imminent disintegration. I also noted one or two standard three-ton lorries. Without exception, the buses were fitted with producer gas plants, also a common feature of Indian vehicles, which would enable them to run without relying upon the small petrol ration given to civilian vehicles.

By no stretch of imagination could they be regarded as being a safe or satisfactory form of transport for well over two hundred men, two 1,200 lb. guns, mortars, shells, ammunition, and other supplies. Yet it could be done, for I have often seen similar vehicles each carrying at least forty persons, and large quantities of stores on the roof, lurching along with the gas plant glowing red hot at the back.

Passing along the line of vehicles, we came to another door leading into a small office, and there the men stopped. The officers entered, half closing the door. The office was lighted a little more brilliantly than the garage, and for the first time I was able to see the Indian clearly. I should have known that he was a Muslim from the red fez which was perched on the top of his bald head; although from his general appearance he might have been anything: bazaar babu, moneylender, minor Government Official or even the local Muslim League organiser. He was very much overweight and was dressed in a badly-fitting suit of soiled European clothes complete with enormous rolled gold cuff links visible below his frayed coat cuffs. Not a very prepossessing specimen. The office was typical of thousands of Indian offices: bare distempered walls, an iron grill for a window, dirty concrete floor stained red with the accumulation of many years of steady betel juice expectoration, a couple of rough forms and tables, and piles and piles of dusty papers, yellow with age, recording the transactions of Suleiman Ismail, his father, and in all probability, his grandfather before him.

After a few brief preliminaries a spirited argument opened between the I.N.A. commanding officer and the garage proprietor; which, from the rapidity with which it developed, seemed to be but a resumption of an earlier argument started whilst we were waiting at the gate.

I could not understand all of what was being said since they spoke in Hindi or Urdu, but the word *chawal* (rice) was repeated frequently, and I gathered that Suleiman Ismail was not willing to supply the rice. I surmised that he only desired that his trucks should be taken, so that, if things went wrong, he could state that they had been stolen by the Japanese.

The argument waxed fierce and long. Mohindar Singh began to lose his temper, and the other adopted a servile attitude, wringing his hands and pleading in a whining voice. Suddenly Mohindar Singh turned upon me in an unreasonable rage:

"Why did you think there was rice here?" he snarled. "This fool says that there is none, and no grain shop either."

Without giving me time to answer, he turned to the garage proprietor again, and proceeded to threaten him in a savage fashion, waving his big fists in the air, and spitting out a stream of rapid Urdu. The wretched man cringed before him, gesticulating feebly in the intervals of wringing his hands.

At that moment there was an interruption as another Indian entered the room leaving the door swinging open behind him. I gazed at him casually, more interested in the brow-beating of Suleiman Ismail. Something about him attracted my attention. Somehow or other I felt that I had seen him somewhere before, but for the life of me I could not tell where or when.

He addressed himself to Mohindar Singh, advancing into the centre of the room beneath the light. He was a small wiry man with sleek black hair, wearing a *dhoti* and blue shirt. There was an air of authority about him as he, ignoring Mohindar Singh's furious questions, proceeded to ask some of his own. A rapid interchange of Urdu followed, with the fat garage proprietor apparently telling his tale of woe to the younger civilian, and the I.N.A. Colonel repeating his demands for rice.

He listened for some minutes and then, cutting the others short, stepped in front of Suleiman Ismail and confronted the tall figure of Colonel Mohindar Singh.

"*Buddha ka chiz, kahan hai* (Where is the Buddha?") he said.

Without a word Mohindar Singh slipped his hand into his pocket, and produced—the brass Buddha. But even before I saw the little brass idol, the cause of all my troubles, I knew. My mind went back to an evening three months earlier on the station platform at Dimapur: a small Indian civilian wearing a blue shirt and a *dhoti*—unquestionably the same man as the one who stood before me now. My heart missed a beat, started again, and then missed another.

The wheel had turned full circle, the Buddha had been returned to the man who dispatched it to Rangoon. As this drama of real life started with this ugly little idol, so it seemed fated to end. I sensed the approach of a climax, and drawing as far back from the dim light as I could, I waited with baited breath.

I had not long to wait.

A few unintelligible words passed between the younger man and Mohindar Singh. I could not understand what was being said, which made it all very horrible, but I was conscious of the steady and inexorable march of events towards a climax—the nature of which I was aware—yet unable to avert. Once again I felt the same strange paralysis creeping over the lower part of my body.

I heard Mohindar Singh mention the name of Maurice Derocque, and saw an expression of bewilderment spread over blue shirt's face as he repeated the name twice. Then all eyes in the room were turned upon me.

I could do nothing but stand and stare at the face of the younger civilian, whose expression of amazement became more marked as he looked at me. Then quite suddenly, a look of fear came into his eyes, and I distinctly understood his next words, even though they were spoken in Urdu.

"I have never seen him before."

As if in the grip of a horrible dream, I gazed spellbound as he drew nearer to me, his eyes fixed upon my face. Suddenly he stopped dead, and a look of terror spread over his face as he gasped out the words:

"Yes—Dimapur—The British Officer."

From the corner of my eye I saw Mohindar Singh's hand fly to the butt of his pistol as he snarled:

"*Jasus ho*! (You are a spy)"

Then the civilian was shouldered to one side, and I was looking down the barrel of his automatic pistol, reading my fate in his deep-set eyes. There was a sharp report, and I closed my eyes expecting that it was the end. But no, there was no pain; and opening them again I saw the tall figure of Colonel Mohindar Singh crumple up and fall to the ground with a thud—and behind him, standing in the doorway, the burly bearded form of Jemadar Gurbaksh Singh, a long Japanese automatic pistol smoking faintly in his right hand

WE SAVE THE SITUATION

FOR a full minute I could only stand and stare at the dramatic scene before me, flabbergasted by the sudden turn of events. At last I realised that this was my cue, and I also whipped out my pistol and covered the astonished Das Gupta and the two civilians. However, my sudden action was scarcely necessary; the fate which had overtaken Colonel Mohindar Singh had struck terror into the hearts of the unhappy conspirators, reducing them to a state of palsied impotence. Captain Das Gupta could only stand and stare, a ludicrous expression of amazement upon his dusky features.

My own former immobility was forgotten and, for the first time, I felt myself to be in control of my future, instead of being the helpless plaything of forces beyond my ken. I realised that the longed-for opportunity had arrived, and now it all depended upon me.

Turning to the bewildered Das Gupta I said:

"Captain Das Gupta, you may consider yourself under arrest, and until you can be handed over to the proper authorities I shall place you in the charge of my men here. If you attempt to escape, you will be shot."

"B-But," he stammered. "What do you mean? We have to get the rice or there will be trouble when we see Major Tagachaki. I don't understand—who are you?"

"My name is Denny," I answered. "I am a British officer."

"Then you are not Derocque—and you are a spy," he gasped, his expression of bewilderment changing to one of fear.

"Colonel Mohindar Singh paid me that compliment, but unfortunately he is not in a position to discover the truth of his statement now."

Whilst I was indulging in this rather reprehensible piece of gloating at the expense of the wretched Das Gupta, I had been watching the two civilians, and had noticed the expression of fear on the younger man's face change to one of desperation. He was like a cornered rat, his dark features set, his black eyes darting in all directions. I knew that he was only waiting for the slightest opportunity, despite the menacing pistols. The jemadar still stood silently in the doorway with the pistol levelled. The other man was quite broken down, and had collapsed on to one of the rough benches, where he crouched with an expression of despair upon his face.

Turning this time to the jemadar I said:

"*Shukria*, Jemadar Sahib. I am grateful for your intervention. You have saved my life."

"It is nothing, Sahib, I was watching him," he replied, his grave features breaking into a smile. "I have done my duty again, after so long, and I have killed him as I swore I would do. What is to be done now, Sahib?"

"For the time being I want you to remain here. I, with two of your men will go for assistance. We are safe, but the Japanese are still on that hill and must be destroyed. What of your men? Are they all to be trusted?"

"Those that are not are too frightened to do anything, and there are but four unreliable," he replied.

"Good," I said. "Now detail four men to guard these prisoners, they must not be allowed to escape. Watch that young man very carefully. I do not like the way he looks. If there is any trouble, shoot him."

So saying I holstered my pistol, and left the room.

The Indian still stood in the same place, his fists tightly clenched and his chest rising and falling convulsively.

Passing the little knot of excited sepoys standing near to the door and beckoning two of them to follow me, I walked down the garage in search of a suitable vehicle. At one end, parked at the rear of the other vehicles, I came upon a large Ford car. Within a few minutes we were swinging out of the gates on to the road. I was looking for some sort—any sort—of a military unit, knowing that the civil police were useless in an emergency of this kind, and having no time to waste in trying to get the Indian telephone system to work.

After speeding along for about ten minutes a large notice-board illuminated by the lights of the car caught my eye: 'Garrison Engineer, Naojan District'. Scarcely checking the speed of the car I swung into a narrow drive alongside the board. Before I knew what was happening I had crashed through a white pole across the drive, overturned a sentry box at the side, and almost run down an Indian *chowkidar* (watchman) who skipped out of the way like a frightened rabbit. Stamping on the brakes, I skidded to a standstill in front of a large bungalow and bounded out of the car.

As I ran up the steps to the front door it opened, and a figure, doubtless attracted by the noise resulting from the unceremonious manner of my arrival, appeared in the opening. Without wasting any words on him I pushed him back, and found myself in a large office. The officer, for that is what he was, followed me into the building spluttering indignantly:

"Who are you?—What do you want? What do you mean by bursting in here in this manner? Are you drunk?"

"Now look," I replied. "I'm neither mad nor drunk, and there's no time for fuss. I must get some assistance quick. Who are you, anyway?"

For a full minute he stood looking at me before he replied. I saw that he was a tall, rather weedy man, with a stooping figure and an unhealthy white face. He wore the badges of rank of a Major. Then he went on, with an air of outraged dignity:

"Before I answer any of your impertinent questions, young man, I demand to see your identity card. I shall certainly write to your C.O. about this. I would not tolerate it from one of my subalterns."

"Please," I said, "I can explain all this. There are five hundred Jap troops on the railway not five miles from here, and no one knows anything about it. I must get in touch with the nearest infantry unit."

"You are drunk," he replied, setting his thin lips in a tight line as he finished speaking. "And if you do not give me your identity card immediately I shall have to place you under arrest. I never heard such nonsense in all my life—Japs—Huh! Besides this I am very busy, and I hope that you realise that you are interfering with my work. I have a directive to write on the latrine-siting policy of the whole Area."

"I have no identity card——"

"You have no identity card," he interrupted, "I wonder if you have reported the loss? There is a Special I.A.O. which lays down the correct procedure."

"For Heaven's sake, listen," I shouted. "There are five hundred Japs near here, and I must get help. Only tell me where I can find the nearest infantry unit. Or let me get them on the 'phone—I see that you have a 'phone."

"If you expect me to believe such a cock and bull story, you think wrong, and I would remind you that you are talking to an officer who is very much your senior."

"It is true—and I have just come from Burma with them," I roared.

"I thought you were drunk, and now I know," he said, his white face darkening with anger. "I have just read the Area Intelligence Summary for inclusion in my Secret file, and there are no Japanese nearer than Kohima. Now will you go."

Losing patience at this priceless gem of crass 'proper-channel mindedness' I caught him by his narrow shoulders and shook him violently, shouting the while:

"Do I look as if I am drunk?"

As he looked at my unshaven face, my haggard worn appearance, some doubt seemed to strike him, and the traces of anger faded from his features to be replaced by an expression of studied competence. He disengaged himself from my grasp, and walking over to a desk seated himself behind it.

"If what you say is true," he said, "I think that I had better take down a statement from you, so that I can submit a report to Area. I have no troops myself, and there is nothing apart from a platoon of Ghurkas here. I will call my typist and that will save time if he takes it straight down. I think that it will be necessary to do it in triplicate—no quadruplicate—I think the Administrative Commandant ought to have a copy. I will do it now, and then it can go off by Signals in the morning."

For a moment I was too astounded to reply. The man was actually thinking of preparing a lengthy report, which he proposed to submit through the slowly but surely flowing official channels—so that the information would be sure to reach the 'appropriate authority' in three days at any rate! That is if some Indian clerk didn't send it to the wrong address.

"Sir," I said, leaning over the desk and pushing my face within about three inches of his pasty features. "You are talking a lot of cock. *This is urgent*. Something has got to be done *now*—and *quickly*. Make as many reports as you like, the Japs are about four miles from here, on the railway in the direction of Dimapur. Just tell me where these Gurkhas are."

"What do you mean? These . . ."

"Where are these Gurkhas?" I roared.

"About half a mile along the road," he gasped. "But——"

"Good; that's all I want to know. Now have you got any sawdust, or anything like that?"

"Sawdust?"

"Yes, *sawdust*. You're the G.E. aren't you? I'm not mad; I want something that I can put into bags to represent rice. See? And I want some bags."

Obviously he didn't see, but he answered me nevertheless.

"Yes, I have got some. There is a saw mill at the back, but what——"

"Right, now do something for me—and don't ask questions. Whilst I am away get as many bags filled with sawdust as you can. I have a purpose behind all this, but there isn't time to explain. Just get it done, that's all —and I'll be back."

Leaving the astonished Garrison Engineer, I rushed out of the building, jumped in the car and shot away past the broken pole with the gaping *chowkidar* still standing there, and out on to the road again.

After travelling a short distance, the half mile mentioned by the G.E., a few tents standing back from the road attracted my attention. It appeared to be the place. I stopped the car and jumped out, my escort following me, and walked across to a tent from which the dim light of a hurricane lamp shone. Before I could reach it I was stopped by a stocky little man, a typical Gurkha, with his big broad-brimmed Gurkha hat perched at an angle on his bullet head.

"*Officer kahan hai* (Where is the officer)?" I asked.

"*Tambu, Sahib*," he replied, pointing in the direction of one of the tents.

"*Muje Lieutenant Sahib ke pas le chalao* (Take me to the Lieutenant)," I said.

"*Ji, Sahib*," he answered, and led the way across to the tent.

Pushing the flap to one side I walked in, and proceeded to shake the recumbent form which lay on the camp bed beneath the mosquito net.

"Wake up," I said. "Japs! Jifs! Come on, wake up."

"Eh! Wass that? Who's there?" he ejaculated, sticking a tousled head from under the net, and blinking in the light of the hurricane lamp held by the sentry.

"If that's you again, Atthara, I'll wring your—— Who in the world are you?"

"Now listen," I said. "And to start off with, I'm not mad. See this"—seizing one of my escort's Japanese rifle—"Look—see, a force of Japs is just on the other side of the railway, five hundred of them, and something's got to be done."

In an instant he was out of bed, a young fresh complexioned fellow, clearly the recent production of some O.C.T.U. He jumped into his clothes, and shouted instructions to the sentry in Gurkhali, now and then pausing to ask me a series of questions. In as few words as possible, I told him as much as I could, skating over my own connection with the whole business as being too difficult of explanation. I brushed aside his question of "What's the matter with you? You look as if you've about had it," and went on to say:

"There are roughly five hundred of them, and I know exactly what their dispositions are and what weapons they have. They intend to block the railway and set up another block on the other side of Dimapur. Suleiman

Ismail was to have supplied the transport, but that little scheme has been knocked on the head. One thing though, they are very short of food, and that is why I came with these men—Jifs they were—to get rice. By now their mules should have been stampeded, and I know that they can't last very long without food. I've a scheme for killing some of them which will help—— Where can we get some more assistance?"

"There is nothing nearer than Dimapur," he replied. "But I can get a message to my H.Q., and we'll get something up by morning."

"Good enough," I said. "Although I think that the G.E. up the road is raising the alarm."

"That old fool!" he answered scornfully. "Still, he might do something I suppose."

I explained my scheme to him whilst he finished his preparations. I was banking on the Japanese not doing anything until we returned with the rice, even though the loss of the mules and the defection of most of the Indians would tell them that something was wrong. By that time it would be nearly morning, and the reinforcements, if they arrived on time, would be able to confine them to the hill and starve them out.

After a message had been concocted and despatched, the Gurkha officer piled his men into a truck, and we set off for the G.E.'s office. On the way he listened with growing amazement as I elaborated my story and, from the questions he asked, I could see that there was a lingering suspicion in his mind that the whole thing was some kind of a hoax. I do not blame him. When we arrived at the office we found the foolish man writing out a lengthy report.

"Ah!" he greeted me. "I shall need a few details from you. What is your name, and number? When did you——"

"How about my sawdust?" I asked, cutting him short.

"I have two of my men filling the sacks at the back; but I still don't know why you want the stuff."

"Two men!" I shouted. "Don't you realise the seriousness of the situation?"

Then, ignoring his protests, we rushed out and doubled round to the back of the building followed by the grinning Gurkhas who seemed to be enjoying themselves immensely. Sure enough, in a large shed we found two weary-looking individuals, one of whom I recognised as the *chowkidar* I had so nearly overturned, filling sacks at a very leisurely rate. They were speedily pushed to one side, and the Gurkhas proceeded to fill the bags at a rapid rate. Leaving them to it, I got into the car again and went back to the garage with the platoon Gurkha officer.

On arriving there I discovered that everything was as I left it, except that the younger Indian civilian was now crouching on the floor, nursing his right arm from which a trickle of blood had run down on to the concrete. In response to my query the jemadar calmly replied:

"He tried to get away, Sahib—so I shot him as you said."

Mohindar Singh still lay where he had fallen.

Leaving four of the Sepoys and the four unreliable Sepoys to act as guard, we started up the two civilian three-ton vehicles, the only two petrol trucks in the garage, and drove back to the G.E.'s office. By this time a large number of bags had been filled with sawdust, and these were carefully loaded on to the trucks, the little Gurkhas piling their arms, ammunition, and last of all themselves, on top.

The night was far spent, and the time somewhere round about three o'clock. I scarcely felt tired, my previous weakness was forgotten in the excitement of the preparations for my counter blow. I considered that the time was just about ripe, it being essential to do what we had to do as near dawn as possible, but before it began to get at all light. We started off. I drove the first truck and the jemadar drove the second one, through Naojan village, passing the turning leading towards Suleiman Ismail's garage, and along the road in the direction of Dimapur.

It was still very dark as the decrepit trucks chugged along, wheezing and coughing, at a steady twenty miles per hour, their maximum speed. About half a mile from the spot where we had first come on to the road after leaving the hill I slowed down, and one by one the Gurkhas dropped off and disappeared into the shadows at the side of the road. I slipped the clutch sufficiently to keep the spluttering engine running at the same speed, just in case there were any listening ears about. At the same steady pace I drove on, and stopped as near to the correct place as I could judge, pulling well on to the verge out of the way of any vehicles which might come along. As I climbed out of the truck and jumped to the ground I was startled by a rustling noise nearby and the sound of heavy breathing: then I realised that it was one of the mules. Evidently Havildar Baquat Ali had done his part.

Leaving the jemadar and his men with the trucks for fear that one of them might even now play me false, I descended the side of the embankment and walked across the paddy in the direction of the railway. Just before I reached it, I was stopped dead by the appearance of a round pudding-basin-like helmet, silhouetted against the lightening sky, and the challenge:

"*Tomare! Utso zo!* (Stop or I shoot)"

"*Tabemono. Isoide kudasai, jikan ga amari arimasen kara* (Food. Hurry up, we have not much time)," I replied, desperately stringing together the few words of Japanese that I knew.

I could not have chosen a more effective answer however hard I tried: the magic word 'food' was the complete 'open sesame' and, without further ado, I was allowed to pass. I picked my way across the railway, and was soon talking to one of the Japanese officers, repeating the same words with the same magical effect as before. I was passed on to Major Tagachaki who, when he heard my good news, was so relieved that he did not even ask me why I had returned alone, but immediately issued orders for a fatigue party to be formed to carry the precious grain to the hill. I could scarcely conceal my satisfaction as I noted the size of the party; not less than one hundred men, for it was very important to get the food on to the hill and the trucks away before it was light, even though the deserting Indians might by this time have revealed the presence of the Force to the British authorities—which was by no means certain. In any case, although the proposed road block on the far side of Dimapur might have to be abandoned, it did not mean that the whole scheme had fallen through. The fact remained that the Japanese were astride the railway, and the longer they were undisturbed the more difficult would it be to dislodge them; particularly now that their food supplies were assured—or so they thought.

I led the way across the fields again with Major Tagachaki trotting along by my side followed by the hastily-organised porters, who were not even armed, so hastily had they been gathered together, blessing my ignorance of the Japanese language and my companions' excitement, which prevented the asking of awkward questions. The dawn was breaking, and the shadows beginning to grow faint as the black bulk of the trucks loomed up before us. My heart was beating like a sledge hammer against my ribs from mingled fear and excitement, and my overwrought nerves caused me to dig my nails into the palms of my hands, drawing blood as I afterwards discovered. It was not pleasant to realise that three Bren guns and twenty or so rifles were trained in my direction, with as many fingers itching on the triggers. Suppose someone was a little bit 'trigger happy'!

We reached the trucks without incident. I saw that the jemadar and his men had disappeared to some place of safety, having lowered the lorry tail-boards to disclose the dimly seen bulk of the piled up bags of 'rice' as I had instructed. At the sight of the food a murmur of satisfaction arose from the hungry Japanese, and without a moment's delay they seized upon the sacks, pushing me to one side, and commenced to unload them. Greatly relieved at my off-handed dismissal, I slipped away into the paddy on the opposite side of the road—and ran as fast as my legs would carry me.

Suddenly the silence was shattered by the roar of musketry as the Gurkhas opened up with everything they had: machine guns, rifles, and grenades, at almost point-blank range from their carefully-sited ambush into the packed mass of Japanese milling around the trucks. The surprise could not have been more complete.

I stopped dead, and turning towards the bunded road saw two trucks silhouetted against the first streaks of dawn in the Eastern sky, and the figures of the Japs running hither and thither in the wildest confusion. Then it seemed as though an invisible scythe swept through their midst, mowing them down in rapid succession from left to right—and the immediate skyline formed by the embankment road was clear, broken only by the black mass of the vehicles and the occasional appearance of a demented Jap soldier, for all the world like a marionette, striving vainly to escape the deadly hail from the still chattering Brens.

For fully two minutes the guns fired as fast as the Gurkhas could change magazines and barrels, and then the firing gradually died away into an occasional burst from the Brens and sporadic rifle fire as some moving target presented itself in the growing light. Then there was silence, broken only by the clearly audible groans of the wounded men littering the road, a series of strangled screams from one man writhing in mortal agony, and the cool clipped tones of the young Lieutenant issuing fresh instructions to his men.

Retracing my steps, I cautiously approached the road, calling out to the Gurkhas to avoid being shot on sight. By this time they had emerged from their places of concealment, and were gathered in a group in the shelter of the embankment refilling the Bren magazines; squat, green-clad figures, grimly intent upon the task in hand. Seeing my approach, their officer came over to me.

"To think I fancied you were pulling my leg," was his greeting. "I've never seen anything like it in my life: it was like shooting sitting pigeons. Ugh! Can you hear them?"

I could hear them. Overcome by a morbid curiosity, I climbed the side of the embankment and beheld the most ghastly sight that I have ever seen. The ground was strewn with dead and dying Japanese, lying in every conceivable attitude, or still crawling and twisting in blind anguish. The air was filled with their groans and cries, and the unmistakable sickly odour of blood and death. Around the trucks they were thickest, sprawling on top of each other and the sacks of 'rice', for the sake of which they had abandoned all caution. As I gazed, horror-stricken, one of them who had been huddled against the wing of one of the trucks struggled painfully to his feet. It was an officer—Major Tagachaki—his long *samurai* sword still hanging at his side, and a great patch of blood on the front of his tunic. With what must have been a tremendous effort, he dragged the sword from the scabbard, gripping the side of the truck for support, and then staggered towards me, his sword waving in his nerveless hand like a reed in the wind. For a dozen or so paces he struggled on, his shadowy features turned towards my own. Then he stopped, his left hand flew to his throat, the sword fell from his grasp clattering on the road, and he pitched forward on to his face.

It was the last straw, and suddenly I was violently sick.

I fled from the scene of horror and rejoined the Gurkha Lieutenant.

"Are you O.K.?" he asked. "You look about all in. You'd better leave things to me now."

"I'm all right," I replied, although I felt quite the reverse. "It's just that my stomach is pretty bad. Give me some water, that's all."

He offered me his water bottle, and after a while I felt a little better.

"You know what will happen now," I went on. "They will put in an attack to get that stuff over there, thinking that it's rice. They must do, it's their only chance, and we can't stop them if they do. Not that they would get anything if we just let them have it, but we must keep them occupied here until somebody comes. If they find out that there is nothing here they might attack Naojan and find some there."

"We can do it," he replied. "They have no idea of our strength yet. For all they know we might be a battalion strong. That means that they will put in a heavy attack with all they've got, if they are as desperate as you say, and that'll take a bit of preparation. I wish that someone would come though before they find out that they've only got a platoon to deal with."

So the platoon was disposed along the embankment, widely dispersed to give an illusion of numbers, and then we waited.

The time passed on leaden wings as the sun slowly appeared over the crests of the hills; but still there was no sign of the reinforcements from Dimapur. Then the expected attack began. The first intimation was the appearance of half a dozen tiny figures on the railway embankment, which was visible across the paddy fields. They advanced with little attempt at concealment, rather obvious decoys, intended to make us open fire and reveal our positions to the real attacking force. The six men continued to advance slowly in extended order, but we ignored them, well aware that the attack would come from one or both flanks, in keeping with the usual Japanese encircling methods. After a while I thought I caught a glimpse of a Jap steel helmet above some bushes over to the left, not more than about four hundred yards away, making me feel certain that an enveloping attack was developing.

The tension was terrific for we were aware of our chances of survival if help did not soon turn up. Had I been a little less agitated, I might have noticed the complete absence of traffic on the road, an unusual thing in an area occupied by large military forces, and wondered if it meant that the traffic had been stopped for a definite purpose. As it was, I merely waited with growing trepidation, conscious only of our extreme weakness, and the strength which the enemy could deploy against us.

Suddenly it started; there was a whistling sound in the air, and with a loud bang a small shell, probably fired from a grenade discharger, exploded on the far side of the road, throwing fragments of tarmac into our midst. Then another, and another, faster and thicker, until the air was filled with reverberating crashes. Almost at the same time a pair of L.M.G.s opened up, firing in short regular bursts, punctuated by an irregular crackle like that of rifle fire, but which was almost certainly made by cannon crackers, exploded with the express intention of making us think that we were already surrounded. Apart from the first lucky shot from the grenade discharger, which landed only about twenty yards from where I crouched, the fire was wildly inaccurate; clear proof that they had no real idea of the location of our position.

The bombardment continued for seven or eight minutes, and then suddenly ceased. As it did so, a party of about ten Japs doubled across the road not one hundred yards away. Quick as they were, the Gurkha Bren gunners were quicker, giving them a long burst which bowled them over like ninepins. That particular party of Japanese had miscalculated badly, otherwise they would never have come into the open at so short a range, but, by their sacrifice, our position would have been revealed, and I knew that we might expect an accurate shower of grenade discharger fire at any moment.

But it never came. At that moment a cloud of dust away along the road in the direction of Dimapur attracted my attention, a cloud which grew rapidly larger, whilst the regular beat of engines and the clatter of tracks became audible. The tanks were coming.

A LEGITIMATE GRIEVANCE

LITTLE now remains to be told. With the arrival of the tanks, the Japanese retreated to their stronghold and fell on the defensive, maintaining some of their offensive spirit for a couple of days by patrolling and engaging any target which presented itself to their four mountain guns. The information which I gave enabled a Section of 25-pounders which was brought up to wreak havoc amongst them, and the Japanese guns were silenced one by one. On the first night they attempted a raid in force on Naojan village, probably in a desperate attempt at obtaining food, but they were beaten back with losses. Their efforts on the second night were less vigorous, clear proof that disease and starvation were rapidly undermining their strength. On the third night, after doing some damage to the railway track, they withdrew, leaving behind almost half of their original number: dead, wounded, or too weakened by disease even to crawl.

Perhaps a handful managed to find their way back over the hills to tell the story of the disaster which had overtaken them, just as they were on the point of accomplishing the purpose of their mission, but the great majority were doubtless doomed to crawl on until, their strength failing them, they collapsed and died, or seeking the more glorious way committed *hari kari*.

In all, about ninety ex-I.N.A. soldiers were rounded up from their wanderings after they deserted the Jap positions. I was instrumental in saving almost all of them from being treated as ordinary prisoners of war.

Most of the former Indian Army men rejoined their old regiments, the jemadar included. I only saw him once more. He came to visit me before proceeding on leave to his village prior to reporting to the Depot of his regiment. He was smartly dressed in a suit of brand new green battle dress, a flash of colour on his left breast from his clean, fresh medal ribbons, a neat green turban, and his walking stick firmly grasped in his right hand. He held himself erect, radiating an air of dignity and self-respect, typical of all that was best in the regular Indian Army N.C.O.

"Salaam, Sahib," he greeted me, saluting with punctilious precision. "I go now to my village. All is well, and I am once more a soldier. It is because what the Sahib has done for me."

"Not at all, Jemadar Sahib," I replied, "I owe my life to you."

After the good fellow had gone, I felt one hundred per cent better for his visit. I had been feeling particularly grim, brooding on what I considered to be a legitimate grievance. That particular morning I had been called to an interview with a Staff Officer at the H.Q. of 33 Corps, recently arrived in the area from Western India. I was shown into his office to find him seated behind a table. He was a sleek dark-haired man of about twenty-eight years of age, sporting a ridiculously overgrown moustache of the 'cavalry' type, wearing a starched and pressed bush shirt and trousers of a glaring lemon colour with striped silk socks and a pair of crepe-soled suede shoes of the type commonly known as 'brothel creepers', on his shoulder the crown and pip of a Lieut-Colonel, and on one arm an armband of green cloth: the starched cuffs of his bush shirt were turned back in an ostentatious fashion, and a kerchief of white silk was tied round his neck to act as a sweat rag. I compared his appearance with that of any member of Wingate's Special Force with a grim feeling of amusement. A typical young regular officer—Acting Lieut-Colonel, Substantive Lieutenant—risen high in the Service as a result of the war-time expansion of the Army and the influx of temporary officers.

His greeting was abrupt, his manner aloof, and without inviting me to take a seat he launched straight into the purpose of the interview.

"The mattah of your connection with the enemy during the period of your stay in Burmah has been carefully considered at Staff level. It is felt that your conduct was, to say the least of it, indiscreet; even considering the exceptional circumstances of the case. Serious consequences might very well have resulted. In particulah, I am instructed to inform you that you have narrowly escaped being charged with a grave offence—I refer to your action in accepting a commission in the I.N.A. Neither do we accept without qualification many of the statements which you have made, but, as it is impossible to disprove them, the whole mattah will be dropped.

"You are a young officah, and perhaps do not realise the seriousness of your actions, yet ignorance is no excuse. The only redeeming featchah of the whole of your conduct is the belated promptness which you displayed at the end. I warn you that you will not escape so lightly if there is any repetition of this kind of thing. You will be watched, and I advise you to watch your step.

"You may go."

I went.

Perhaps I was fortunate, perhaps I was the victim of forces outside of my control, and perhaps I was not. When I read the account of the court martial of Stoker Rose, one of the traitor John Amery's dupes in the German-inspired British Free Corps, I realise that I was skating over very thin ice. Rose was tried on three counts: of treacherous correspondence with the enemy—of which he was found guilty, and on two counts relating to the communication of intelligence concerning Radar and the Boom Defences of Portsmouth—of which he was found not guilty.

With the tinge of unfairness that is so often characteristic of courts martial, the Prosecuting Officer had maintained that, although it was clear that any information given by Rose concerning Radar was false because he knew nothing, it did not alter the fact that he was a traitor. For, he said, he was charged with giving 'intelligence' to the enemy, and the dictionary definition of 'intelligence' is information, with nothing added to say whether the information shall be true or false.

Fortunately for me, that did not happen in my case. If it had happened I am quite sure that my attitude would have been like unto that of the ancient malefactor whose frame of mind is quaintly expressed in the account of a certain court martial:

> 'In that he at Rawul Pindee, on the 8th day of October 1883, when checked by Sergt. Thomas Snell of the same Regt, stepped from the ranks, threw down his arms, and said: "You may do as you please, but I will soldier no more"—or words to that effect!'

It is not possible to over-estimate the gravity of the blow which the Japanese cause sustained by the failure of their efforts in the Imphal-Kohima area: the very gateway to India. Without doubt their advance across the border marked the highest level of the flood tide of their success. Apart from the actual military set-back, the consequences of which proved to be far-reaching, things were not going too well for them in the S.W.

Pacific, and Tokyo was looking for a quick victory to bolster up the nation's morale; the invasion of India had been intended to fulfil that purpose. If the Japanese could have effectively cut the Bengal-Assam railway anywhere between Dimapur and Ledo, they would have dealt the Allies a well-nigh mortal blow; they would not only have cut the main lines of communication for General Chennault's U.S. Air Forces operating over the 'Hump' in support of Chiang Kai Shek's armies, but also the main supply route of General Stilwell's road-making and combat forces then working down the Ledo Road.

The whole situation around Kohima had been delicately balanced in the extreme, the perimeter defences had been driven in and the garrison all but isolated. As it was, on the 1st April the British Second Division reached Dimapur from India unhindered; the 161 Indian Infantry Brigade having arrived a few days earlier. After twelve days of hard fighting the cordon around Kohima was smashed, and the garrison which had been reinforced when the British Regiment of the 161 Brigade broke through the enemy ring, was saved; and so, it is probable, was the whole sub-continent of India.

I have often pondered the whole matter of my connection with Major Tagachaki's Task Force and wondered if it did have some effect on the ultimate outcome of the whole campaign. I cannot but feel that they would probably have reached their goal without my unwilling assistance, but then again I suppose that I did put some sort of a spoke in their wheel at the end. It is sufficient for me to know that the tide did turn, and the Japanese were forced to begin the disastrous retreat which ended with the annihilation of their 15th and 28th Armies and the liberation of all Burma.